The Collegiate HEPCATS

This homage to Mœbius' "The Detour" was drawn especially for a lousy local sci-fi fanzine called *Trajectories*. (Don't worry, it's long dead.) The editor called dozens of local cartoonists soliciting work for a special comics issue he wanted to have out for the 1988 San Diego Comic Con. Unable to get the money together to print the issue, he then absconded with everybody's original art for over a year.

MARTIN WAGNER

The Collegiate

HEPCATS

Double Diamond Press

AUSTIN, TEXAS

Dedicated with love to my parents

Tom & Teri Lynne Wagner

who have always supported my artistic endeavors,
even when they haven't understood them.
(Which is a lot of the time.)

Also, special thanks to the many fans and retailers whose generosity over the years has helped keep
Hepcats going, and has made this book possible.

Couldn't have done it without you.

THE COLLEGIATE HEPCATS
Volume 1 of the Hepcats Reprint Library

A Double Diamond Press Publication
Printing History:
Hardcover edition: May 1993
Paperback first edition: May 1993
Direct market paperback first edition: December 1993
ISBN 0-9636660-0-2 (paperback)
      0-9636660-1-0 (hardcover)

10 9 8 7 6 5 4 3 2 1
93 94 95 96 97 98 99

Printed in the United States of America by BookCrafters., Inc., Fredericksburg, VA.

Syllabus

Introduction
TO THE DAILY HEPCATS
BY MARTIN WAGNER

The book you hold in your hands is the first volume of the Hepcats Reprint Library, what will ultimately be a multi-volume compendium of what I could pretentiously call my life's work. It shouldn't be so pretentious a phrase, really. Every artist has a life's work, every politician, scientist, bricklayer. Each of us has a calling. Some of us become corporate executives, or airline pilots, or television talk show hosts. Some mechanics, restauranteurs, clergymen. And some of us draw talking animals.

It isn't the most glamorous job in the universe. And it certainly doesn't pay well. But for a dedicated artist it can be enough. I don't live in a freezing garret. I have a comfortable apartment with a good central air unit, a laserdisc player, lots of books and a toilet that flushes properly about every third try. I also have a blue sketchbook that continues, after many years' healthy use, to serve as an excellent icebreaker with the fair sex. Everybody I know who has a "real job" gripes about it until my ears swell and bleed. Idiotic bosses who work you to the bone for little reward and not nearly the pay you deserve...and then, of course, there's the harassment factor if you're a woman. No, ma'am, give me my apartment, my drawing table, and my loyal fans. I'll eat. I'll do just fine.

Hepcats was created in May 1987 and premiered on June 1, on the comics page of *The Daily Texan*, the student newspaper at the University of Texas at Austin. I was 21. As I write this I am almost 27 and the changes almost six years can bring are cataclysmic. Anyone who has followed the current comicbook incarnation of *Hepcats* for its (as of this writing) 11 issues has read in my editorials of the tempestuous roller-coaster ride that has been my life. Now, I am pleased to report things are calmer—not quite the teacup ride, more like bumper cars. But I have brought my little comics creation into the world, and though it has been a difficult endeavor I do not regret one moment of it. *Hepcats* has survived hardships that would have killed virtually any other comic book, and I'm not bragging about how that makes me great—simply demonstrating my unshakable muleheadedness. Because this is my calling. My life's work. And if it interests you, this is the starter kit. Read on.

The Daily Texan in the late 1980s was an interesting place to cartoon. Having come from the modest operation of the University of Houston's *Daily Cougar*, I had it in mind to do a strip that would not be quite so campus issues oriented as my UH strip, *Shasta Says*, had been. I wanted to tell stories about real characters, real *people*, to whom readers could relate from the heart. However, having drawn humanized animals for years, I sought to bring forth such personalities into the character designs I'd grown accustomed to drawing. Whether I have been successful is, I imagine, up to your personal taste, but *Hepcats'* varied and vocal fan following has comforted me that there *is* an audience out there for this kind of stuff, and luckily I've plugged in.

The Daily Texan is a jarring experience for first-timers, sort of like drinking six cappucinos and then peeing onto an exposed electrical wire on a dare. Somewhere in its history the *Texan* got it into its adorable web-pressed head that it was Austin's second newspaper, and ever since then its staffs have been trying to run it as such, in an aggressive, high-tension manner befitting, I suppose, what they feel running a real city paper must be like. The youthful exuberance and enthusiasm you might expect to find in a venture manned by college kids has been subordinated to an often oppressive, fifth-gear "this is the real world" vibe that can be ulcer-inducing if you let it get to you. Still, my two years there exposed me to a fascinating variety of human fauna, most of whom I remember fondly.

Everyone calls the *Texan* a clique. Actually, it is several cliques, each of which is so sharply delineated I expected the various departments to start nailing Greek letters above their office doors on many occasions. The staff camaraderie I enjoyed at the *Cougar* was not really there. (Of course, the *Cougar* had the endearing quality of being staffed entirely by goofballs, and the fact they managed to get a daily paper out at all borders on science fiction.) Sports was a clique, though a chummy, palsy-walsy one, which you might expect from sports nuts. And true to form, Entertainment was such a venomous, xenophobic, unfriendly clique they might as well have put barbed wire and hungry, unfixed Dobermans around the office door—exactly the sort of atmosphere you'd expect from 19-year-olds who write record reviews. While I was there, the entire Entertainment staff was on a mission from God to discredit U2, which led to some enjoyably incendiary salvos from students in the letter column. How could we cartoonists mind that "Firing Line" was frequently funnier than anything we managed to come up with? Anyway, I think the chief appeal of Entertainment was being able to dig through the pile of free albums record labels would send.

News was a clique populated by harried journalism undergrads (the only journalism majors on the staff) who rarely looked up from their CRTs as they tried to beat deadline. I can't recall ever having had occasion to say a word to any of them. No, wait—I dated Robin for a couple of months. And Editorials...whoof! There's a story. At the time, two "editorial page editors" overseeing a small staff of op/ed writers, customarily populated by a gang of sitcommish stereotypes: The Feminist, who kept us all up to date on the latest sexist media images so we wouldn't miss out; The International Student, who'd be unleashed any time our military accidentally blew someone up in the Mid-East; The Gay Guy, who kept us all entertained by giving the campus Republicans apoplexy; The Campus Republican, who kept us all entertained by giving gays, women, and minorities apoplexy; and so on. The howls of righteous rage any one of these folks would elicit from "Firing Line" gave rise to a new spectator sport worthy of the Olympics.

Moving up the editorial food chain, you found the assistant managing editors. An a.m.e.'s job principally consisted of running "slot" (the threshold through which all copy, artwork, etc., must pass before paste-up) and dashing from office to office at ten minutes to deadline, theatrically hyperventilating. Though this provided amusement for tired staffers it never did much to get things out on time. In my two years at the *Texan* the paper made deadline all of twice. Finally there was the managing editor and the editor, two genuinely overworked, overstressed individuals, whose jobs consisted of seeing who could collect the most grey hairs before their 23rd birthdays.

We cartoonists were at the bottom of the food chain, and a clique all our own, though we often crossed over into other groups because occasionally someone would want a drawing or something. We weren't part of the Graphics department, but naturally we hung out in the graphics office, a room almost as small as my bathroom. At one point during my tenure my fellow cartoonist Van Garrett was Graphics editor; at another, a lovely and charming girl named Ashley who cut up with all of us to pass the time waiting for an a.m.e. to burst into the office and wail like a man demented that a certain word in the front page pie chart wasn't capitalized.

It was in this interestingly compartmentalized milieu that *Hepcats* evolved from a gag strip to the alternative graphic-novel-oriented comic most of you know today. Certainly, there were mostly outside influences upon my life that would manifest themselves in the creative aspects of the work, but the *Texan* taught me some valuable things.

· I hope to heck I never have a real job.

· Editors, like Nazis, are people too.

Still, though I work largely alone today, I did learn to work among people, work around people, and work with people, and when you work with people who do what you do you learn from them, and the learning benefits your work. I mentioned a couple of years ago in *Hepcats #1—The Special Edition* that one negative trait I brought with me from UH was an insufferable ego, something that working in the *Texan* environment—I hope—pounded into submission.

The late 80's *Texan* comics page is largely thought of (not just by me, honestly) as the last good comics page the paper ever had. The late 70's-early 80's had Berke Breathed and Sam Hurt. We had Chris Ware (who's gone on to *Raw* and various other critic's darlings of the alternative comix scene), John Keen, Marc Trujillo, Van Garrett, Tom King (creator of the transcendentally sick "Dream Date Trading Cards"), and film student Robert Rodriguez, whose action flick *El Mariachi*—which he filmed for less than it cost to publish this book—made him the toast of Hollywood in 1993 and our group's first Actual Famous Person. After my departure came Walt Holcombe, Korey Coleman, Jeanette Moreno, and Harvey nominee Shannon Wheeler. Then, mostly, silence. Then again, I don't see the *Texan* much anymore, so perhaps there's a new young talent getting ready to emerge.

A quick overview of the two-year run: The earliest work is highly and unabashedly derivative, stylistically, of *Doonesbury* and *Bloom County*. The reason for this is, of course, that I was just starting and a cartoonist just starting is going to ape the work he is fondest of. It's all part of educating yourself and some artists do it to a greater degree than others. The Trudeau/Breathed style was hot-hot-hot in the early to mid 80's, and frankly, it was easy. Given its ease of execution and immense popularity I am really surprised that most newspaper strips of the time remained lamely generic to the point of nonexistence, when they could have hopped the bandwagon to the million-dollar saloon. Maybe for the same reasons I don't do superhero comics today, though I like to think my alternative is a worthy one. Still. Early into the fall 1987 semester I began reading comic books again, and black and white indies for the first time ever. *Cerebus* quickly became a favorite, as did the Epic graphic novels of Mœbius, and I began slowly learning how to do more precise, detailed work, less interested now in newspaper cartooning. Things moved quickly, and by the fall 1988 semester (page 76, strip 1—page 93, strip 2) I was growing bored of the limitations of the four-panel format. This was the weakest semester of the run, in my opinion. I wanted to do a comic book, and so I began drawing the first issue of *Hepcats* in November 1988, finishing it around February-March 1989. Fulfilling this passion got the coagulating artistic juices flowing again, and I think I returned to form for the final semester, spring 1989, the principal storyline of which involves the birth of Joey's little sister Rachael. Also, I had by this time made the decision to pursue self-publishing, so I had that feeling of exuberance combined with melancholy that accompanies a major rite of passage through life (graduation, marriage, etc.). I knew that the loyalists would follow the characters to the new phase, but for most readers, well, they'd never see Joey and Gunther and the gang again. So I did what I could to make it special and memorable. These characters are, after all, my family.

The inspirations for my characters, as well as my early formative years at the drawing table, were described to the point of anal-retention in the "Hepcats History 101" chapter of *Hepcats #1—The Special Edition*. Since, with the publication of this volume, I plan to let that issue go happily out of print, I'm aware this may not help fans first discovering *The Collegiate Hepcats* in, say, 2002. Right now, with the final printing of *H1—TSE* fresh off the web, there are still plenty of these circulating, but for future readers, I may be nice and include this chapter in an upcoming volume of the Hepcats Reprint Library.

But. In the last year or so I have become quite a fan of laserdiscs, the album-sized CDs that display movies with full digital sound and a ridiculously crisp widescreen picture (even starving artists deserve one indulgence), and one aspect of the technology that fascinates me is the ability of directors to give running commentaries on their movies on a magical secondary audio channel you activate with the mere press of a button. Sometimes this is self-indulgence but often it yields fascinating behind-the-scenes information. Since books do not have audio channels at all (thank god something is still sacred) I cannot do this. However, assembling this book has proven to be a nostalgia trip of surprising proportions. Much of this art I haven't seen in five years, and I've now been doing *Hepcats* long enough that I'm coming upon strips I've forgotten. Every once in a while a strip will activate a particularly potent memory cell. Therefore I have included a supplement immediately following the strips, to shed light and reveal some background that may be of interest to fans. In doing so, I have attempted to include only that material I think may actually be of interest, and avoid the indulgence trap altogether. Given that this work is so personal to me, I hope the generous reader will excuse me if I do, on occasion, slip.

So here you have it. The first volume. The starter kit. If this is truly your first exposure to *Hepcats* I welcome you aboard and hope what you find is to your liking If so, do stick around. We've only just begun.

Cover drawing for the *Texan*'s Holiday Gift Guide, December 1, 1988.

HI, FOLKS! THOSE OF YOU WHO HAVE BEEN READING THIS PAPER FOR A WHILE MAY HAVE NOTICED. WE'RE NEW AROUND HERE. THAT'S WHY WE FELT INTRODUCTIONS WERE IN ORDER.

OKAY! SO! THIS IS "HEPCATS." I'M RORY AND THAT'S STEVE, AND YOU CAN FIND US EVERY DAY IN "THE DAILY TEXAN" ON PAGE... UH...

HANG ON! HANG ON!

WHAT'S WRONG? ...OH, GREAT! DID THEY EVEN PUT US IN?!

WAIT A MINUTE... HERE WE ARE!

"S.W.M., 28, SEEKS IDENTICAL ORIENTAL BONDAGE TWINS FOR PARTY GAMES AND..."

NO, NO. UNDER THAT. SEE?

As CONFUCIUS (OR SOMEONE LIKE HIM) ONCE SAID, THE JOURNEY OF A THOUSAND SUMMER VACATIONS BEGINS AT THE "PULSE" MACHINE.

JOEY McLYON

PLEASE ENTER IDENTIFICATION CODE

BEEP BOOP BEEP BLIP

ACCOUNT BALANCE: $-344.76

UNABLE TO COMPLETE THIS TRANSACTION.

ALSO, WE'RE VERY VERY DISAPPOINTED IN YOU, JOEY.

SPIT!

HAS THIS EVER HAPPENED TO YOU? IF SO, YOU'LL RECOGNIZE THE SLOW, SINKING FEELING...

MR. McLYON? WHAT A COINCIDENCE! I'M WITH YOUR BANK.

GUNTHER! I'VE GOT TO DO SOMETHING TO MAKE SOME MONEY, DUDE, OR MY BANK'S GONNA HAVE MY SKIN!

The SHAFT Apartments

WELL, IT'S YOUR FAULT, SPENDING LIKE A ZILLIONAIRE. WHY DON'T YOU FIND A JOB?

AW, DUDE! I DON'T WANNA GO TO WORK!

WELL, CAN'T HELP YA, BUD. I WOULDN'T WORRY ABOUT IT TOO MUCH. SOMETHIN'LL TURN UP.

MEANWHILE...

YOU KNOW, RORY, MAYBE WE SHOULD GET JOEY A VISA CARD.

SPEW!

DID I JUST HEAR YOU CORRECTLY? YOU WANT THAT CRAZY KID TO CARRY AROUND MAJOR PLASTIC?

HE'S ALMOST 20. I THINK IT WOULD BE GOOD FOR HIM TO ESTABLISH CREDIT.

JUDY, YOU'VE FLIPPED! THAT KID GOES THROUGH MONEY FASTER THAN RONALD REAGAN!

WE'LL PUT A LOW LIMIT ON IT. IT'LL BE EDUCATIONAL!

EDU-? HERE'S SOME EDUCATION! SEE THIS? IT'S OUR PHONE BILL! $322! JUST FOR LAST MONTH! ALL THIRD-PARTY CALLS!

YOU COULD HAVE TOLD HIM TO CUT IT OUT, RORY.

SEE THIS? IT'S MY WALLET— EMPTY! BIG ★⊕≶!!☺ DIFFERENCE, I'D SAY!

WHEN YOU'RE READY TO TALK SENSIBLY, LET ME KNOW.

KLANK

ROAR

SMASH

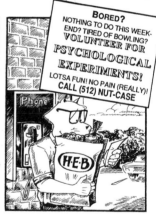

Undaunted by the fears of his elders, Steve went to the clinic, filled out all the applicable forms, and started his career as a "guinea pig."

THANK YOU FOR VOLUNTEERING, MR. GOLD. IF YOU'LL STEP THIS WAY, WE CAN GET STARTED.

SURE!

HI, STEVE!

THIS IS CANDACE. SHE'S GOING TO ASSIST WITH THE FIRST EXPERIMENT.

JESUS!

CRUNCH!

WHOOF!

PRETTY MIXED SIGNALS, HUH? HOW DO YOU FEEL?

...OH, I CAN'T FEEL MUCH OF ANYTHING RIGHT NOW, THANK YOU.

HEY! WHAT THE?

AH, MR. GOLD. SO NICE TO SEE YOU'VE COME AROUND.

WHAT ARE YOU QUACKS UP TO?

WELL, WE'RE TESTING TO SEE IF EXTENDED PERIODS OF BEING HUNG UPSIDE DOWN PRODUCE UNDUE STRESS.

SO HOW LONG AM I GONNA BE LIKE THIS?

NOT LONG. ONLY TEN DAYS OR SO.

TEN DAYS?!

IF YOU NEED ME, I'LL BE AT A SYMPOSIUM IN CHICAGO.

HEY! C'MON! THIS ISN'T FUN ANYMORE! ALL THE BLOOD'S RUSHING TO MY #@*!¿%@ HEAD!!

I'M GETTING TUNNEL VISION, YOU ASSHOLES! CUT ME DOWN!

SNAP

BONK

ALL RIGHT! I'M MAD NOW!

HE'S MAD, DOCTOR!

MAYBE THERE'S A CORRELATION HERE.

JO—
—EY...

JOEY?

COME ON... WAKE UP.

...HUH?

HEY, WOW! I MADE IT! I'M IN THE HOSPITAL!

I'M ALIVE!

DOCTOR, HE'S COMING OUT OF IT!

JEEZ! DID I REALLY WRECK A LAMBOURGHINI?

MY DAD'S GONNA BLOW ME AWAY!

LOOKS LIKE THE DOCTOR. WHAT'S HE TRYING TO SAY?

JOEY? YOUR PARENTS ARE HERE!

UH-OH! TIME FOR A RELAPSE!

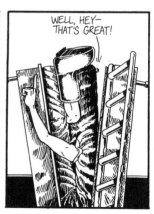

ANYWAY, I WAS THINKING OF ABOUT TEN SHORT SCENES DEPICTING DOMESTIC SITUATIONS BEFORE AND AFTER SEPARATION AND DIVORCE.

I'VE GOT FRIENDS WHO'LL AGREE TO BE IN 'EM, I'M SURE. THEN YOU CAN SHOOT 'EM WITH YOUR CAMCORDER — VOILA, INSTANT PRESENTATION TOOL!

SCENE 1: "MOTHER CONFESSES." SCENE 2: "WHAT IF THE KIDS OVERHEAR?" SCENE 3: "DELINQUENT DAD." SCENE 4...

THESE SOUND LIKE PORNO LOOPS, JUDY.

OO, YEAH! I BETTER ADD A FEW PRONOUNS!

CASTING CALL—

C'MON, RORY, WHY DON'T YOU WANT TO BE IN THE VIDEO?

I JUST DON'T, OKAY, JUDY? CAMERAS GIVE ME A RASH!

KNOCK! KNOCK!

AW, HONEY. DON'T YOU WANT TO SHOW OFF THAT CUTE MANE? WIGGLE THOSE WHISKERS? BE AS BIG A HAM AS YOU LIKE? RORY?

WELL, FINE, **BE** THAT WAY...! RORY? ...**RORY?**

YOU'RE SURE? ABSOLUTELY NO "SUPER-SAVER" FARES TO ANTARCTICA?

NO, SIR. HOW ABOUT CHEYENNE, WYOMING?

KNOCK! KNOCK!

SUBURBAN DALLAS, DAY...

WELL, JUDY, THAT SOUNDS FUN. LET ME ASK KEN.

KEN!!

WHAT?

IT'S JUDY McLYON! SHE'S MAKING SOME FAMILY-CRISIS VIDEO AND WANTS US IN IT!

WHO DO WE FREAKIN' LOOK LIKE — BURTON AND TAYLOR?

I JUST THOUGHT IT'D BE FUN!!

THOUGHT? YOU HAD A THOUGHT!? HOLY SHIT!

ANGIE, LET ME CALL BACK.

CHUCK, THIS IS CHERYL, RORY'S SISTER. SHE'S AGREED TO BE IN ONE OF THE SCENES.

GREAT!

HI, CHUCK.

CHERYL'S BEEN THROUGH ALL THIS DIVORCE STUFF. YOU MIGHT SAY SHE'S BEHIND THE PROJECT.

OH... UH...

YEAH, WITH ANY LUCK, I WON'T NEED A LOT OF COACHING.

SURE, WHATEVER YOU SAY.

SAY, THIS IS PRETTY TAME STUFF. SHOULDN'T I BREAK A FEW WINDOWS?

NOT ON OUR BUDGET.

YOU **ARE** INTO THIS!

...AT LONG LAST, SHOOTING GETS UNDERWAY.

NOW, CHERYL, I TOLD YOU WHEN YOU MARRIED THIS GUY HE WASN'T ANY GOOD, BUT...

LOOK, DAD, I KNOW HE'S A SON OF A BITCH, BUT THIS SOMETHING THE KIDS AND I HAVE TO WORK OUT ON OUR OWN.

WELL, YEAH, YOU'RE RIGHT.

CUT! LOOKS LIKE A KEEPER! WHADDAYA SAY, JUDY?

OH! HOW COME?

NOPE. DO IT OVER.

I'M SHOWING THIS TO P.T.A. GROUPS, CHERYL. YOU CAN'T SAY "SON OF A BITCH."

GOD, I'M SORRY, JUDY! MEMORIES...

SCENE TWO...

...SO, ESSENTIALLY, NICK, YOU'RE BRIBING YOUR SON WITH THIS STEREO SO HE'LL TELL YOU WHAT YOUR EX-WIFE'S BEEN UP TO. NOW, I WANT TO SEE SOME SUBTLE INTERPLAY HERE, OKAY?

BAUHAUS Sale.

ACTION!!

SO, YA LIKE THIS ONE?

SURE, DAD!

audio

SO, YOUR MOM SEEING ANYBODY?

I DUNNO.

CUT!

TOO SUBTLE?

TALK TO EACH OTHER, GUYS! IF I'D WANTED CLINT EASTWOOD, I WOULD HAVE HIRED HIM!

SCENE THREE...

HI, JUDY. SORRY I'M LATE.

THAT'S OKAY. THIS IS KEN AND ANGIE FROM DALLAS.

HELLO, CHUCK. NICE TO... KEN!

I TOLD YOU TO KEEP THESE KIDS IN LINE!

WAAH!

IT'S HER FAULT!

OH! SO THE KIDS ARE ALL MY RESPONSIBILITY, HUH?

JUDY, LET ME TALK TO YOU IN PRIVATE.

MONEY, JUDY! NOT 12-PACKS! MONEY! LOTS OF IT! UP FRONT!

CHUCK, IF I'D KNOWN THIS WOULD BE SUCH A HASSLE...!

JUDY, I HAVE AN IDEA. YOU NOTICED HOW THE LITTLE GIRLS WERE MAKING ANGIE GET REALLY UPTIGHT?

UH-HUH?

WELL, WHEN WE START ROLLING, BRING THEM INTO THE NEXT ROOM AND HAVE THEM MAKE LOTS OF NOISE! IT COULD GET SOME HONEST ANGER INTO THE SCENE.

OO! OKAY!

WOW!

WHAT IS IT?

I JUST REALIZED! I REALLY ENJOY MANIPULATING PEOPLE!

SEE!? YOU'RE THE HITCHCOCK OF THE '90'S, CHUCKIE-BOY!

PINCH!

17

Judith A. McLyon
A.C.S.W.
invites you to the
World Premiere of
"Breaking Up"
Sunday 1 P.M.
RSVP
Dress Hollywood!

YES, THE VIDEO THAT IS DESTINED TO REVOLUTIONIZE MODERN DIVORCE THERAPY IS ABOUT TO MAKE ITS DEBUT.

HEY, I MADE IT! Y'ALL CAN START PARTYING NOW!

CHUCK!

SAY, YOU PULLED IN QUITE A CROWD!

YOU BET! WE HAVE LOTS OF FOOD, CHUCK, AND RORY'S MAKING THE PUNCH.

ISN'T THAT AN AWFUL LOT OF VODKA, RORY?

TRUST ME... YOU'LL NEED IT TO SIT THROUGH THIS!

WELL, I REALLY WANT TO THANK EVERYBODY FOR COMING! "BREAKING UP," BY THE WAY, IS CHUCK'S DIRECTORIAL DEBUT!

SO THIS IS THE GUY WE CAN ALL EMBARRASS WHEN HE CLINCHES HIS FIRST OSCAR, RIGHT?

THANKS.

CLAP CLAP CLAP CLAP

OKAY, SO WE'LL JUST PRESS "PLAY" AND GET STARTED...

WAIT... CHUCK, DID YOU HIRE THESE GIRLS IN G-STRINGS?

I THINK WE GOT ONE OF RORY'S TAPES BY MISTAKE!

UH, YEAH, I'M, UH, SAVING IT FOR JOEY'S BACHELOR PARTY SOMEDAY....

HEY, LET'S SEE THIS!

JUDITH ANN PRODUCTIONS
presents
BREAKING
UP
FAMILY DYNAMICS OF SEPARATION AND DIVORCE

Produced by
JUDITH ANN McLYON
A.C.S.W.

· Directed by
CHUCK WALLACE

©1987 by Judith Ann Productions

THIS IS A
JAP
PRESENTATION

OH, NO...

OO, NEAT! SHE SHOT HER CREDIBILITY IN THE FIRST NINETY SECONDS!

SHH...

DUNNO WHY-Y I LOVE YA LIKE I DEWWW... DUNNO WHY-Y-Y I FE-E-EEL SO BLUUUUE... DARLIN', YA KNO-O-OW THAT IT'S TRUUUUE... BREAKIN' UP IS HARD TEWWW DEEWWWW...!

WELL, CHUCK! IT LOOKS LIKE "BREAKING UP" IS A SUCCESS!

WELL, THAT'S GREAT. AND I HOPE IT DOES WELL FOR YOUR PRACTICE.

YOU KNOW, I'VE ALREADY HAD A FEW CALLS FOR PRESENTATIONS. THE IDEA HAS REALLY CAPTURED PEOPLE'S IMAGINATIONS!

WHAT ABOUT YOU? WHAT'S UP NEXT? HOW IS YOUR SCRIPT COMING?

WELL, JUDY, I JUST KEEP AT IT. IT'S A LONG, HARD ROW TO HOE.

WELL, LOOK, I WAS THINKING OF DOING ANOTHER VIDEO THIS FALL...

GREAT. I'LL TRY TO BE HAVING BRAIN SURGERY OR SOMETHING.

Part I

A GUIDED TOUR OF Martin Wagner's HEPCATS

PART I

A 4-PART SYNOPSIS-cum-INTRODUCTION FOR NEW READERS

·Your Host·
Rory McLyon

©PAT MLS 25 AUGUST

HI, KIDS! AND WELCOME TO "HEPCATS"! AS YOU MIGHT HAVE NOTICED, WE'RE THE NEW STRIP AROUND HERE, SO I THOUGHT I'D BETTER SHOW YOU AROUND!

ACTUALLY, WE MADE OUR DEBUT IN THIS FINE PAPER BACK ON JUNE 1st, 1987... SO THOSE OF YOU WHO PARTIED ALL SUMMER BACK HOME WILL WANT TO BE

THE DAILY TEXAN
Tammy Faye Bakker dies of asphyxiation

MGM buys movie rights to 'UT 16' for $6.5 million

BROUGHT UP TO DATE.

SO FOR THIS FIRST WEEK, WE'LL LET YOU IN ON ALL THE MAJOR CHARACTERS AND THEIR THRILLING EXPLOITS, WHICH DO NOT INCLUDE THE SCENE ABOVE, UNFORTUNATELY.

TOMORROW, WE'LL GET STARTED! AND YOU CAN FIND US DAILY, RIGHT THERE BELOW THESE GUYS.

Part II

· A 'MIS'GUIDED TOUR OF Martin Wagner's HEPCATS PART II. YOUR HOST: Rory McLyon. ©1987 MLS 26 AUGUST. ·

WELL, KIDS, I GUESS YOU KNOW WHO I AM, SO LET ME INTRODUCE YOU TO THE REST OF THE LEADS.

THIS IS **JUDY**, MY RICH WIFE. SHE'S A PSYCHOLOGIST, AND SHE MAINLY DOES MARRIAGE COUNSELING. SO SHE MAKES $63,000 A YEAR OFF OF PEOPLE WHO HATE THEIR SPOUSES. I LOVE JUDY!

ANYWAY, JUDY JUST FINISHED UP A VIDEO PROJECT WITH THIS MOVIE NUT NAMED **CHUCK**, WHO AT AGE 37 IS STILL SEEKING HIS "BIG BREAK".

...AND HE JUST MAY GET IT, BECAUSE HE'S FINISHING A SCREENPLAY BASED ON HIS EXPERIENCES IN **VIET NAM**. AND SINCE NAM IS HOT PROPERTY IN HOLLYWOOD THESE DAYS, HE **MIGHT** SELL THIS ONE! WE'LL SEE.

SO, WHO'VE I LEFT OUT...?

OH, YEAH. MY KID.

Part III

A GUIDED TOUR OF Martin Wagner's **HEPCATS** PART III

Your Host:
Rory McLyon.

OKAY, SO I MAY AS WELL GET THIS OVER WITH. THIS IS MY SON, JOEY. HE'S KIND OF A DORK.

©1987 MLS 27 AUGUST

JUDY & I STILL GET INTO ARGUMENTS OVER WHOSE FAULT HE IS. FOR EXAMPLE, IN ONE AFTERNOON, HE TOTALLED A $260,000 SPORTS CAR, PUTTING ME IN DEBT FOR THE NEXT 433 YEARS.

I MEAN, THIS IS A DANGEROUSLY STUPID KID, Y'ALL.

JOEY'S ROOMMATE IN COLLEGE (WHERE HE HAS STAYED OFF SCO-PRO, TO MY AMAZEMENT) IS GUNTHER. A PARTY RHINO WHO STUDIES NOW AND THEN.

HE'S ALSO FALLEN IN LOVE, I HEAR. SOME GIRL NAMED MONICA. I SMELL CATASTROPHE ON THE WIND.

IT'LL BE NEAT TO SEE HOW LONG JOEY CAN MAKE IT...

DESPITE HIS ENTHUSIASM, JOEY KNEW THAT JOINING A FRAT WASN'T SOMETHING HE WAS PREPARED TO DO ON HIS OWN. SO...

ME!? HA HA! GET REAL!

GUNTH! COME ON! YOU LIKE TO PARTY! THINK OF WHAT YOU'LL MISS!

JOSEPH. DESIST.

GUNTH, THINK OF THE **BABES**! GIRLS! WOMEN! RHINETTES ALL **OVER** THE PLACE!

SURE ENOUGH, THIS LAST PITCH DID THE TRICK. GUNTHER THOUGHT LONG AND HARD, KNOWING HIS DECISION WOULD HAVE A PROFOUND EFFECT ON HIS LIVELIHOOD.

BUT IN THE END, HIS ANSWER HELPED PROVE AN AGE-OLD SCIENTIFIC THEORY WHICH HAS PLAGUED ZOOLOGISTS FOR YEARS:

RHINOS ARE, IN FACT, BIG STUPID ANIMALS.

OH, **WHY NOT**!

DUDE!

THUS THE NIGHT OF THE TRI-LAMBDA RUSH PARTY ARRIVED ...WITH JOEY McLYON AND GUNTHER IN ATTENDANCE.

IT WOULD BE AN EDUCATIONAL EVENING IN MANY WAYS.

"ANCIENT CANTONESE TORTURE TECHNIQUE."

HMM-MUST BE A CLASSICS MAJOR.

YOU! PUT THAT DOWN!

FOR IN EVERY LIFE COMES A MOMENT SIGNALING A FINAL, SHATTERING LOSS OF INNOCENCE.

THEY WHAT?

THEY WANT US TO COME BACK. THEY SAY THEY'VE GOT 75 MORE KEGS AND...

4:01

FOR SOME MORE EMBARRASSING THAN FOR OTHERS.

TOPLESS DANCERS.

TOPLESS DANCERS! **SWEATY** TOPLESS DANCERS!

BUT YOU GUYS GOTTA COME OVER **NOW**!

THIS BETTER BE GOOD, JOEY.

YO! WE'RE BACK! WHERE'S THE GIRLS?

AWESOME! **HEY, OUR PLEDGES ARE BACK DUDES!**

WE THOUGHT WE'D THROW YOU DUDES YOUR **VERY OWN** PARTY, 'COS WE'RE SO PROUD TO HAVE YOU IN THE FRAT!

HUH?

COOL!

THE DAILY TEXAN

Editorial Notice We have informed Mr. Wagner that if he wants to hang on to his goolies he'd better make it doggone clear that the fictitious fraternity depicted in his comic strip, which is about to engage in a fictitious hazing activity, is in **no** way meant to represent an actual frat at this University.

It's common knowledge that **none** of our fine frats would **ever** involve themselves in any situation in which people could get hurt or even killed. Right? Right.

—S. S. Pryce
God-Emperor, Daily Texan

GOOD SHOT, TODD!

NO WAY THEY COULDA KNOWN WHAT HIT 'EM!

COME ON! HELP ME GET 'EM INTO THE TRUNK OF MY CAR

THUS A FEARSOME FRATERNITY RITUAL KNOWN AS "THE RIDE" TAKES PLACE IN THE WEE HOURS OF THE MORNING.

LATER, AFTER THE GRUELING RITE OF PASSAGE, A LONE CAR SPEEDS THROUGH DARKENED, EMPTY STREETS.

SCREEE...

TODD... ARE THOSE PLEDGES GONNA BE OKAY?

SURE THEY ARE! JUST GET OUR BUTTS BACK TO THE HOUSE!

I-I'M JUST NOT SURE WE SHOULDA LEFT 'EM LIKE... **THAT!**

MEANWHILE...

WELL, GUNTH. WHAT'RE WE GONNA DO?

I'M GOING TO FIND SOMETHING HEAVY TO HIT YOU WITH -WHAT'RE **YOU** GONNA DO?

27

28

29

For you see, dear readers, Chuck Wallace's life is one riddled with moments of dissatisfaction and self-doubt.

JEEZ, CHUCK, WHAT'RE YOU DOING IN THIS PLACE?

Joe's Tavern

SO YOU FINISHED YOUR BIG SCRIPT. WOW. SO HAVE 50 MILLION OTHER PEOPLE.

YOU'RE 37. YOU'RE A CLERK IN A LAW OFFICE. YOU GOT NO PROSPECTS.

♪ U GOT THE LOOK...

So sometimes he can forget he has true friends.

CHUCK!

SOLO! GOD DAMN! WHAT ARE YOU DOING HERE? THIS IS A YUPPIE BAR!

I'M SLUMMING! SCOOT OVER, MOVIE MAN!

BARTENDER! A SHOT OF "MAD-DOG" FOR MY FRIEND!

CHUCK'S NARRATIVE:

"AFTER WE'D BEEN AT THE BAR A WHILE, SOLO & I WENT BACK TO MY PLACE, AND WE SHOT THE POOP UNTIL 2:30."

SAY, YOU WOULDN'T KNOW WHERE I COULD GET A ONE-SHEET FOR "SURF NAZIS MUST DIE"?

WELL, I KNOW THIS GUY UP IN DALLAS WHO SELLS POSTERS...

"SOLO'S REALLY A HELL OF A GUY — MAYBE A BIT WILD LIFESTYLE-WISE, BUT PRETTY SHARP. AND A BIG MOVIE BUFF, WHICH IS WHERE WE CONNECT."

OH, DID YOU REALIZE TOM SELLECK WAS ONE OF THE DEAD BODIES IN "COMA"?

REALLY!

"I HADN'T SEEN HIM FOR A FEW MONTHS BEFORE THAT NIGHT, AND FOR SOME REASON I GOT TO THINKING ABOUT WHEN I FIRST MET HIM."

"IT WAS WHEN I WAS LIVING IN L.A., BACK IN '82."

"IT WAS A DAY THAT BEGAN AS WEIRD AS IT ENDED..."

HELP YOU?

YEAH! CAN I RENT YOUR PLANE?

F37071A

CHUCK REMEMBERS:

"YEAH, I GUESS WAS KINDA DESPERATE IN THOSE DAYS. I'D JUST FINISHED A SCRIPT I WAS REALLY PROUD OF..."

NOW WHERE YA WANT ME TO GO AGAIN?

F3707A

"AND WITHOUT AN AGENT, WELL, NO STUDIO WAS GONNA GIVE ME THE TIME OF DAY..."

JUST KEEP GOING STRAIGHT, RIGHT OVER THAT COMPLEX OF BUILDINGS.

HEY, THOSE ARE THE MGM LOTS, AREN'T THEY?

"SO ONE DAY, I JUST DECIDED THAT IF I WAS GONNA GET ANYWHERE IN THE MOVIE BIZ, I'D HAVE TO SOMETHING REAL ATTENTION-GETTING..."

YEP. NOW WHO DO I MAKE THIS CHECK OUT TO AGAIN?

"KYLE'S COURIER SERVICE."

"LIKE PARACHUTE RIGHT ONTO THEIR HEADS."

OKAY, GUESS I'LL BE JUMPING OUT NOW! THANKS!

LATER, DUDE.

"DOWN BELOW, THE GREAT MACHINE OF HOLLYWOOD CHUGGED ALONG AS USUAL."

4

"UPON THE MIGHTY SOUND STAGES, BIG-BUDGET DRIVEL WAS BEING PREPPED FOR THE ELUSIVE LOWEST-COMMON-DENOMINATOR..."

BUT MR. SPIELBERG, THAT GOES AGAINST ANY KIND OF LOGIC OR STORY COHESION...

JUST PUT IT IN, OKAY? THIS IS A TEAR-JERKER, REMEMBER?

"MEANWHILE, FROM THE SKY, CAME HE WHO WOULD BRING ART!"

YA KNOW, I COULD GET ARRESTED ALL TO HELL FOR THIS.

Panel 1: "MY MOMENT OF TRUTH WAS UPON ME. SOON I WOULD PLOP DRAMATICALLY ONTO THE LAP OF TINSELTOWN ITSELF!"

FWUF!

Panel 2: "I DIDN'T MIND THE INEVITABLE JAIL TERM ANY MORE. I JUST WANTED SOME WAY OF GETTING NOTICED."

Panel 3: "BUT ONE THING THAT I FORGOT TO TAKE INTO ACCOUNT AT ALL IS THE FACT THAT L.A. IS A CITY OF UNKNOWN VARIABLES..."

Panel 4: "LIKE THE SANTA ANA WINDS, FOR EXAMPLE."

WHOOPS! WHOA! HEY!

Panel 5: "SO THERE I WAS, BLOWN OFF-COURSE BY A FREAK RUSH OF WIND."
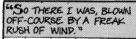

Panel 6: "AND INSIDE THE STUDIOS, THEY CONTINUED TO REMAIN OBLIVIOUS TO THE IMMENSE, UNTAPPED VEIN OF TALENT THAT WAS CHUCK WALLACE."

Panel 7: "MEANWHILE, SAID VEIN (i.e.: ME) WAS WONDERING WHERE THE HELL HE WAS GONNA COME DOWN."
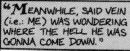
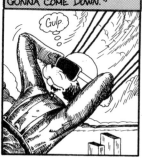
Gulp

Panel 8: "THREE BLOCKS AWAY, MY DESTINY AWAITED."

TONIGHT BLACK FLAG HUSKER DU
THE SPIT CLUB

Panel 9: "THE CHARMING ESTABLISHMENT KNOWN AS 'THE SPIT CLUB' WAS DOING BUSINESS AS USUAL THAT NIGHT."

Panel 10: "THRONGS OF ENERGETIC PATRONS CAVORTED MERRILY TO THE PULSE OF SUCH MUSIC AS CASEY KASEM TRIES TO IGNORE."

SLAM! SLAM! SLAM!

Panel 11: "AND AS I MADE MY RATHER NOISY AND UNWELCOME ENTRANCE, I RECALL ONLY ONE THOUGHT SPINNING THROUGH MY MIND..."

CRASH

Panel 12: YOU KNOW, IF I ACTUALLY SURVIVE THIS, IT'LL MAKE ONE **HELL** OF A SCRIPT!

Panel 13: "HOURS MUST HAVE PASSED BEFORE I WOKE UP."

WHOA! TAKE IT EASY, MAN... YOU'VE HAD A ROUGH ONE.

Panel 14: WHA... WHERE AM I?
MY NAME'S SOLO. JUST RELAX. I DRUG YOU BACK HERE AFTER THE DEAL AT THE CLUB TO MY PLACE. 'DRINK THIS! YOU'LL WAKE UP!

Panel 15: THIS IS **PURE ETHANOL!**

FLOOM

Panel 16: "AND THAT'S HOW I MET SOLO."

YOU WOKE UP, DIDN'T YA?

BACK TO THE PRESENT:

SO YOU FINISHED THE BIG VIET NAM SCRIPT, HUH?

YEAH! AFTER FOUR YEARS! LET ME SHOW YOU REAL QUICK...

SOMETHING WRONG?

YEAH, IT'S **GONE!** THE DAMN DISC HAS **VANISHED!** I HAD IT RIGHT HERE!

HEY, SETTLE DOWN. MAYBE YOU LEFT IT IN YOUR GLOVE COMPARTMENT OR SOMETHING...

NO! UH-UH! I NEVER KEEP MY SOFTWARE ANYWHERE...

ATTENTION!
WRITERS! STORYTELLERS!

The preceding panel included a crucial storytelling element called the **inciting incident.** In fact, it's so important that if you forget about it, you won't have a plot at all and your story will end up boring everyone pooey.

DON'T MEAN TO GO OFF ON A TANGENT OR ANYTHING, BUT THIS WAGNER GUY CAN BE A REAL SMARTASS, YA KNOW?

AND HE GETS ON **MY** CASE FOR HOLDING UP THE STRIP!

BUT BEFORE WE EXAMINE CHUCK'S SUDDEN CRISIS, LET'S GET BACK TO JOEY AND GUNTHER. YES, THEY ARE OUT OF JAIL, AND FITTING BACK INTO LIFE, AS IT WERE.

OH, OKAY, MONICA... SO HOW ABOUT SATURDAY NIGHT...?

YEAH...OKAY... WELL, HAVE FUN...I'LL CALL YOU SOMETIME. SEE YA.

KLIK

AW, **GEE!** SHE DIDN'T HAVE PLANS **AGAIN,** DID SHE?

SHUT UP. SHUT UP. SHUT UP. SHUT UP. SHUT UP.

I DON'T KNOW, GUNTHER. I DON'T KNOW WHAT'S GOING ON IN MY HEAD.

YEAH, WERE YOU & MONICA EXACTLY BOYFRIEND-&-GIRLFRIEND, OR WHAT?

WELL, I'M...I DON'T **KNOW!** WE GO OUT SOME, AND SHE GOES OUT W-WITH OTHER GUYS, BUT—

YOU'RE STILL IN LOVE WITH HER.

※ Sigh ※ YEAH. DAMMIT, I **HATE** BEING IN LOVE. IT'S LIKE, WHAT I'M LOOKING FOR IS JUST OUT OF REACH. IT'S ALWAYS LIKE THAT. I WISH I DIDN'T HAVE TO WORRY ABOUT IT!

GOD, WHY CAN'T I BE AN INSENSITIVE EGOTISTICAL BASTARD LIKE ALL THE OTHER GUYS MY AGE?!?

NOW, NOW, JOEY, YOU'RE CLOSE ENOUGH.

SO JOEY'S HAVING THE SAME OLD RELATIONSHIP HANG-UPS AGAIN?

IT'S WORSE NOW, AL.

OH, YEAH?

YEAH. NOW HE'S TURNING INTO A "SENSITIVE MALE."

WHOA, DUDE!

TELL ME ABOUT IT!

I READ ABOUT THOSE DUDES IN "PLAYBOY." IS IT TRUE GIRLS ARE GOIN' FOR 'EM?

WELL, I HEAR THERE **IS** STILL A BIG DEMAND FOR JERKS LIKE US!

AS DAYS PASSED, GUNTH TRIED TO HELP JOEY FORGET HIS TROUBLES...

COME ON, JOEY! FORGET ABOUT HER! IT'S ONLY GONNA MESS YOUR MIND UP.

I KNOW. I WISH IT WAS EASY TO DO.

GIVE IT TIME! YOU KNOW, I BET WHEN MONICA SEES YOU GETTING ON WITH YOUR LIFE, **SHE'LL** COME AFTER YOU!

HA. THAT'S A LAUGH....

WELL, FOR GOD'S SAKE, QUIT FEELING SORRY FOR YOURSELF. YOU'RE NOT THE ONLY DUDE AROUND WITH PROBLEMS!

THAT'S TRUE, I GUESS.

GOOD GUESS.

LOOK, MAYBE YOU LEFT IT IN THE BATHROOM OR SOMETHING?

NO! WHY WOULD I TAKE MY SCRIPT INTO THE BATHROOM?

COME ON, CHUCK. DON'T FREAK OUT ON ME. COME ON. SIT DOWN.

I CAN'T BELIEVE THIS! M-MY SCRIPT HAS VANISHED!

SIDDOWN. SIT! SIT!!

FOUR YEARS! FOUR YEARS OF SWEAT AND TOIL...

ARE YOU CHILL?

...I'M CHILL.

OKAY. SO WHO COULD'VE STOLEN IT?

I DON'T KNOW, BUT THEY'RE GONNA DIE SCREAMING!

YOU KNOW, SOLO, YOU MAY BE RIGHT...

...MAYBE SOMEBODY **DID** STEAL THAT DISC... IN FACT, NOT LONG AGO I WAS AT A **SCREENWRITER'S WORKSHOP**...

...THERE WAS THIS GUY SAID HE **REALLY** ADMIRED MY SCRIPT... I **COULD'VE** HAD MY DISCS ON ME...

...AND HE **COULD'VE** SWIPED IT, BUT HOW CAN I BE SURE!?

WELL, I COULD BREAK INTO HIS PLACE, AND...

NO! FORGET I SAID **ANYTHING!**

THE NEXT MORNING, A PHONE CALL STIRS CHUCK.

YEAH?

CHUCK, IT'S SOLO! CAN YOU BE DRESSED IN 20 MINUTES?

HUH?

I WANT YOU TO MEET A COUPLA FRIENDS OF MINE—I THINK WE CAN GET YOUR SCRIPT BACK!

SOLO— NOW WAIT—

HEY, DON'T BE SUCH A WORRIER, MOVIE MAN! SEE YA IN A MINUTE!

WHY DO I GET THE FEELING I'M ABOUT TO GET INTO **PILES** OF TROUBLE?

I GOTTA GET THE GAGS FROM SOMEWHERE, CHUCK!

AND WHY WOULD THESE FRIENDS HOLE UP IN A DILAPIDATED OLD WAREHOUSE, HUH?

OKAY, THEY'RE WANTED IN 16 STATES BY THE F.B.I.—BUT IT'S NOT LIKE A BIG **DEAL**, OKAY?!

SHOULD I ASK WHAT **THEY** HAVE TO DO WITH FINDING MY SCRIPT?

LOOK, THEY'RE **REAL** COOL WHEN YA GET TO KNOW 'EM!

DESPITE HIS MISGIVINGS, CHUCK DECIDED "WHY NOT?" AND FOLLOWED SOLO INTO THE OLD BUILDING.

DON'T WORRY, CHUCK! WOULD I DELIBERATELY GET YOU IN TROUBLE?

NO COMMENT.

HONEST, CHUCK, YOU'LL LIKE THESE GUYS! I'VE KNOWN BLACK AND DECKER EVER SINCE THE FIRST SEX PISTOLS ALBUM CAME OUT!

YEAH?

HEY, DUDES! IT'S SOLO! REMEMBER ME!?

LOOK, I BETTER WAIT IN THE CAR, OKAY?

ONCE INSIDE, NERVOUS INTRODUCTIONS WERE MADE.

BLACK, THIS IS MY BUDDY CHUCK. HE'S OKAY, I SWEAR!

AND THIS IS DECKER.

UH...SO HOW'S IT GOING?

AND THIS IS MAX.

HUH?

MAX. HIS PET FIRE AXE.

AIN'CHA GONNA SHAKE MAX'S HAND?

SOLO! SOLO!

DON'T SHOW FEAR—MAX CAN SENSE IT!

SOLO THEN TELLS BLACK & DECKER OF THE LOST DISC.

...AND THERE IT WAS, MISSING, AND CHUCK HAD SPENT FOUR YEARS OF HIS **LIFE** ON IT!

BUT, THERE'S THIS OTHER WRITER GUY THAT CHUCK SAYS MAYBE **SWIPED** IT! SO I TELL MYSELF:

"SOLO, IF THIS DUDE IS GONNA STEAL YER FRIEND'S **ART,** THEN IT'S UP TO YOU TO **STEAL IT BACK!"**

WHAT!?

LOOK, ALL WE DO IS GET INTO THE DUDES PLACE, LOOK AROUND FOR A BIT...

SO WE GET TO DO SOME CRIMES?

NO!

CAN'T YOU SEE HOW EMOTIONAL THE POOR GUY IS?

WELL, MAX LOOKS LIKE I GET TO SHARPEN YOU **UP!**

37

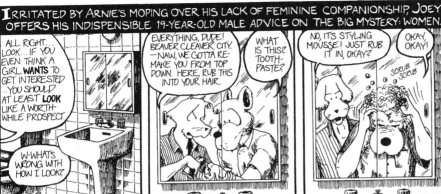

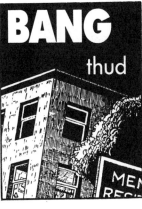

MARTIN WAGNER 1987

WELL, MR. McLYON, I'M **SO** HAPPY YOU DECIDED TO SIGN UP WITH US.

LEMME GUESS, YOU'RE CINDY, RIGHT?

YOU BET! AND LET ME TELL YOU, I JUST **KNOW** YOU'RE GOING TO ENJOY OUR FAST, FUN FITNESS PROGRAM!

$215 A YEAR!?

RORY...

BUT WHEN YOU THINK ABOUT IT, MR. McLYON, IT'S MONEY YOU'VE SPENT ON YOU!

FOR THIS PRICE YOU COULD AT LEAST HAVE A CO-ED SAUNA!

RORY!

PERHAPS YOU'D RATHER TRY FAT SUCTIONING, SIR?

SO WHAT MADE YOU DECIDE TO GET INTO THIS LINE OF WORK, CINDY?

TEACHING AEROBICS, YOU MEAN?

WELL, FITNESS IS LIKE, A MISSION.... YOU KNOW, OVER 70% OF WOMEN IN AMERICA ARE DIS-SATISFIED WITH THE WAY THEY LOOK?

...AND THAT'S SAD. IT'S ALL ATTITUDE, ANYWAY. PEOPLE COME TO US 'COS WE CAN MAKE 'EM BE THE BEST THAT THEY CAN BE!

WELL, STUPID ME. I WENT TO COLLEGE FOR THAT.

—WHERE?

OOF!... TOUCH... ONE... TWO...

♪ BAD... I'M BAD... YOU KNOW IT... ♪

SNAP SNAP

PERSONALLY, I DON'T FIND THIS THE LEAST BIT FUNNY.

ETHEL, WHAT'S WRONG?

THAT NICE MR. McLYON THREW HIS BACK OUT!!

MR. McLYON! ARE YOU ALL RIGHT?

OOHHH...

COME ON, GIRLS, LET'S MOVE HIM TO THE BENCHES!

CAREFUL!

OW! OW! OW! OW!

LOOK OUT! WE'RE TIPPING HIM!!

OH, MR. McLYON! ARE YOU HURT!?

WHY, NO, LADIEFF! DON'T BE FILLY!

SYNOPSIS:

The Subject — A MISSING MICROFLOPPY.

Its Contents — A BRILLIANT SCREENPLAY, FOUR YEARS OF HARD LABOR ON THE PART OF **CHUCK WALLACE.**

IN HIS PANIC, CHUCK JUMPS TO THE CONCLUSION THAT THE SCRIPT MAY HAVE BEEN STOLEN BY A JEALOUS FELLOW WRITER.

THIS GIVES CHUCK'S MODERATELY WILD FRIEND **SOLO** (middle) THE IDEA TO STEAL THE SCRIPT BACK FROM THE ALLEGED THIEF. SOLO ENLISTS THE AID OF HIS SKINHEAD CHUMS, **BLACK & DECKER** (L).

SOLO'S PLAN, OF COURSE, BACKFIRES MISERABLY, SENDING AN ALREADY DISTURBED CHUCK FLEEING THE SCENE ON FOOT AS POLICE CARS APPROACH...

SOLO, BLACK, & DECKER ARE UNDERSTANDABLY MIFFED.

I GET BOTH HIS KNEECAPS.

WHAT DO I GET?

I KNOW! WE'LL TIE HIM TO THE BACK OF MY CAR...

AT CHUCK'S APARTMENT...

JEEZ! I CAN'T BELIEVE ALL THAT ACTUALLY JUST HAPPENED.... MAYBE I'LL WORK IT INTO A STORY ONE OF THESE DAYS.

WELL, I MIGHT AS WELL CLEAN UP A BIT AROUND HERE. WHAT A **MESS!** IT'S NO WONDER I CAN'T FIND MY—

GOOD LORD! MY SCRIPT! WAS IT REALLY UNDER ALL THESE PAPERS ALL THIS TIME!?

BETTER BOOT THIS BABY UP... MAKE SURE... YEAH, YEAH, IT'S ALL THERE!

TYPE WHIRR TYPE KLIK

THANK GOD! THANK GOD! THANK GOD!

THUMP THUMP THUMP

WELL, I GUESS I CAN BREATHE A BIG SIGH NOW THAT ALL **THAT'S** OVER!

KNOCK KNOCK KNOCK

A KNOCK AT THE DOOR INTERRUPTS CHUCK'S RELIEF...

THIS'LL BE SOLO AND THE GUYS, I BET. BETTER TELL 'EM THE GOOD NEWS.

SOLO! GUYS! GUESS WHAT! MY SCRIPT WAS ON MY DESK THE **WHOLE TIME!** WE WENT TO ALL THAT HASSLE FOR NOTHIN'! IS THAT FUNNY OR **WHAT!!**

MCCULLOUGH

TUNE IN TOMORROW, BOYS & GIRLS, WHEN CHUCK MAKES AN HEROIC AND SPECTACULAR ESCAPE THROUGH HIS VERY OWN BEDROOM WINDOW!

RRRR

AT JOEY McLYON'S APARTMENT.

OKAY, MOM. SEE Y'ALL NEXT WEEKEND. AND TELL DAD TO TAKE IT EASY.

DID SOMETHING HAPPEN TO YOUR DAD?

HE THREW HIS BACK OUT DURING HIS AEROBICS CLASS. HURT HIMSELF REAL BAD, I THINK.

OH, MAN! DID YOUR MOM SOUND PRETTY UPSET?

NAAH. MY MOM ISN'T EASILY FAZED. I'M SURE SHE'S HANDLING THIS IN HER USUAL PROFESSIONAL MANNER.

HUSBAND?

OHH— ON THE RECLINER, I SUPPOSE.

OHH, RORY— RORY, I'M SO SORRY THIS HAPPENED.

ABJECT MISERY ↓

OO-O-OH

LISTEN, DON'T WORRY ABOUT A THING! HERE'S A BLANKET, AND SOME STUFF TO READ, AND THE T.V. REMOTE CONTROL— IF YOU NEED ANYTHING ELSE, YELL—OKAY, HON?

—JUDY!!

YES?

I HAVE TO GO TO THE BATHROOM.

JEEZ. FIRST SERIOUS EXERCISING I'VE EVER DONE, AND **SNAP!**— I'M LAID UP FOR GOD KNOWS HOW LONG....

WELL—I DON'T REALLY HAVE ANY RIGHT TO BE MAD AT JUDY FOR GETTING ME INTO THIS. SHE WAS JUST LOOKING OUT FOR ME.

MIGHT AS WELL LOOK AT THE BRIGHT SIDE—

IT CAN'T GET ANY WORSE.

RORY!! GUESS WHAT! JOEY'S COMING HOME FOR THE WEEKEND!!

MEANWHILE, GUNTHER TRIES TO RE-ADJUST TO THE JOYS OF LIFE AS A FULL-TIME STUDENT.

THAT'S THE STUPIDEST THING I'VE HEARD IN MY LIFE!!

WELL, I'M SORRY. I CAN'T LET YOU HAVE THIS MATERIAL WITHOUT A VALIDATED I.D. CARD.

LIBRARY

SO...? I'VE BEEN BUSY! I HAVEN'T GOTTEN AROUND TO IT YET! C'MON, I WOULDN'T BE TRYING TO CHECK THE STUFF **OUT** IF I WASN'T ENROLLED!

I KNOW THAT AND YOU KNOW THAT, BUT THE COMPUTER'S DON'T KNOW THAT.

SCREW THE COMPUTERS! THIS IS MY **GRADE**! I ONLY NEED THE BOOK FOR TWO **HOURS**!

SORRY! I CAN'T DO **ANYTHING** IF I DON'T GET A POSITIVE I.D. FROM YOU!

OKAY, **FINE!** HERE'S A QUICK URINE SAMPLE!

LOOK, I DON'T MAKE THESE RULES UP!!

ADÍOS, GUNTHER! IT'S BEEN REAL.

JOEY! WHAT DO YOU THINK YOU'RE DOING!? GET YOUR ASS DOWN FROM THERE!

MONICA'S JUST LED ME ON, FOR 7 MONTHS! SHE'LL REGRET IT NOW!

NO SHE WON'T! NOW, COME ON INSIDE!

OH, I GET IT! ARNIE TRIES SUICIDE AND EVERYBODY'S SYMPATHETIC, BUT WHEN I TRY...

ARNIE WAS A SERIOUS DEPRESSO CASE! YOU'RE JUST A DORK!

OKAY, WORLD! IF YOU DON'T CARE NEITHER DO I!!

LISTEN, JUST TRY NOT TO SPLAT ALL OVER THE HOOD OF MY CAR, OKAY?

GOOD LORD, JOEY. HOW CAN YOU BE SO MORONIC? IF YOU WANT TO DO THE RIGHT THING, JUST BREAK IT OFF WITH MONICA.

COME ON, GUNTHER! WHAT DO YOU KNOW ABOUT IT?

I TALKED TO HER OVER THE WEEKEND, WHILE YOU WERE AT HOME.

HUH?

SHE SAID THE WHOLE RELATIONSHIP WAS A MISTAKE, AND SHE SAID SHE HOPED YOU'D JUST GO AND FIND SOMEONE YOU COULD BE HAPPY WITH.

EXCUSE ME. I'M JUST GONNA FLUSH MYSELF DOWN THE COMMODE.

THAT'S IT! GO OUT IN STYLE, I ALWAYS SAY!

ANOTHER SYNOPSIS:
SMALL-TOWN RESIDENT **STEVE GOLD** IS THRILLED TO SEE HIS SISTER **DONNA** AGAIN AFTER MANY YEARS, BUT ALARMED TO HEAR SHE IS GETTING MARRIED...

FURTHER ALARM IS REGISTERED WHEN STEVE MEETS THE PROSPECTIVE GROOM, AN UNDERSIZED, OVERWEIGHT LITTLE KIKKER NAMED **JASPER**.

UNABLE TO UNDERSTAND WHY HIS FAMILY SUPPORTS SUCH A MIS-MARRIAGE, STEVE TURNS TO SIMPLE COMFORTS OF PARANOIA—

—AND SINCE STEVE'S GRANDMA HAPPENS TO OWN A LOT OF MINERAL-RICH LAND, STEVE BECOMES SUSPICIOUS OF JASPER'S MOTIVES FOR THE MARRIAGE.

IN ALL, THE WEIRDNESS OF THE WHOLE SITUATION BEGINS TO REMIND STEVE OF SOME OLD EPISODE OF "THE OUTER LIMITS."

STEVE! COME LOOK AT DONNA'S DRESS!!

THAT'S IT! MY WHOLE FAMILY HAS TURNED INTO POD PEOPLE!

THE WEDDING PREPARATIONS CONTINUE AS PLANNED.

AUNT JENNY?

HMM?

IS IT JUST ME, OR IS STEVE ACTING KIND OF STRANGE LATELY?

WELL, HONEY, I'M SURE IT'S NORMAL.

BIG WEDDIN' COMIN' UP... KINDA BRINGS OUT A SIBLINGS PROTECTIVE INSTINCTS. WHY, MY OLDER BROTHER WAS THE SAME WAY.

BUT DID YOUR OLDER BROTHER SIT UP ALL NIGHT TALK-ING TO A BOWL OF POWDERED DOUGHNUTS?

HE MAY HAVE, HONEY. I SURE AS HELL DIDN'T CARE!

NEED COUNSEL? ENCOURAGEMENT? SUCCOR?

GET AT LEAST THE FIRST TWO FROM

DEAR HEPCATS

Dear Megan:

My boyfriend is really putting the pressure on to, like, sleep with him, right? But I'm not sure I'm ready. Please give me some hints cos, you know, what if he dumps me?!!!??!

Timid

You know, honey, men come in all shapes and sizes (yes ha ha very funny Monica) but the one thing they have in common is that they're all typical. Not only is this true but some men are more typical than others, and the one thing they're all predictably typical about is sex, which they're pretty constantly obsessed with and can't get enough of and never will, even though they probably would if they weren't so typical about it.

Anyway, what it sounds like you're really worried about is the ugly likelihood of something like date rape, to which I usually have three foolproof solutions.

MEGAN'S DATE RAPE PREVENTION TOOLS

GOOD

BETTER

BEST

WRITE US! WE THINK WE KNOW EVERYTHING!

DEAR HEPCATS

Dear Joey:

I'm a college student like you, so I want to ask, are all professors mentally divorced from reality or what?

What I mean is, my History prof just assigned *nine* textbooks! And with the average book bill being 73 million dollars and 99 cents anyway this extra load doesn't help. Don't profs know how hard it is to scrape up enough cash for tuition, rent, utilities and all that stuff without throwing *this* on?

I'm seriously considering shoplifting. Please advise.

Broke Plan II Grad

Fig. 1
(inadvisable)

Dear Broke:

No, dude, don't shoplift, really. I mean, especially textbooks. They're usually real big and heavy and solid and if you stick nine of them down your pants, not only does it give you a pretty unconvincing bulge but we're also probably talking Hernia and Vasectomy City.

Also, you might not know this but when you buy books these days, you're on television! *Really.* Look up at the ceiling next time if you don't believe me. So not only will the police and FBI see you, but also millions of viewers and perhaps your parents, too. So do what I'd do. Drop the class.

Joey McLyon

DUE TO ALL THE MAIL *DEAR HEPCATS* RECEIVES REQUESTING ADVICE ON "LIVING ON YOUR OWN," WE PRESENT THIS HELPFUL TWO-PART SEGMENT:

JOEY & GUNTHER'S APARTMENT SURVIVAL GUIDE

In the kitchen

Here are some great basic recipes!

OLD FASHIONED BUTTERED TOAST
Ingredients: Bread, butter, toaster.
Method: Put bread in toaster. Push down prong thingy. When prong pops up, toast should be done. Spread on butter with knife. If smoke alarm goes off, toast is overdone.

DEEP DISH PIZZA
Ingredients: Coupon, telephone.
Method: Call whomever's cheapest. Scrounge in drawers, laundry for cash.

BEER
Ingredients: Beer.
Method: Open bottle. Drink. Repeat as necessary.

FIRST AID TIPS

MOSQUITO BITE
· Squash mosquito.
· Scratch bite until inflamed.

ACNE ON BUTTOCKS
· Shower before going to bed.

FINGERS CHOPPED OFF IN CUISINART
· Scream.
· Fall over.
· Scream some more.
· Pass out.

PREGNANCY
· REMAIN CALM!
· Disconnect phone in case parents call.
· Get telephone list of everyone who was at previous night's frat party.

JOEY & GUNTHER'S APARTMENT SURVIVAL GUIDE PART II

ROOMMATE WARS

Roommate Wars are a fundamental part of apartment living and should thus be conducted in a manner befitting any time-honored ritual. As usual, we have a few indispensable pointers.

WHAT TO FIGHT WITH YOUR ROOMMATE ABOUT

· Whose turn it is to clean the pubic hair out of the shower drain.
· Where the hell their half of the rent is. (Be prepared to come up with alibis should you be the one questioned.)
· Who gets exactly what shelf in the fridge.
· Remembering not to leave dirty underwear hanging from the ceiling fan when company is due.

Here are some suggestions for those inevitable moments when there's *nothing* to do!

· Blow things up in the microwave.
· Rent some movies and tape "Late Night with David Letterman" over them to irritate whoever rents them next.
· Throw a big party, wake up all the neighbors, bust the whole place into a million pieces, get evicted, become a transient.
· Abuse your roommate's calling card number.
· Abuse your roommate if you catch him with your calling card.
· Sleep.
· Watch TV.

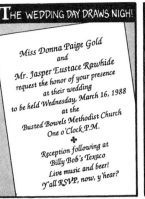

THE WEDDING DAY DRAWS NIGH!

Miss Donna Paige Gold
and
Mr. Jasper Eustace Rawhide
request the honor of your presence
at their wedding
to be held Wednesday, March 16, 1988
at the
Busted Bowels Methodist Church
One o'Clock P.M.

✦

Reception following at
Billy Bob's Texaco
Live music and beer!
Y'all RSVP, now, y'hear?

FAMILY AND FRIENDS GATHER AT AUNT JENNY'S HOUSE. AS THE EVENT DRAWS LOVED ONES TOGETHER AGAIN.

AND AS IN ANY SMALL TOWN, THE WEDDING BECOMES A LOCAL *cause celebre.*

Busted Bowels Daily Ointment • March 14,

WEDDING ANNOUNCEMENTS

Gold, Rawhide to wed

Miss Donna Paige Gold, daughter of the late Erasmus Gold, will marry Mr. Jasper Eustace Rawhide this Wednesday at the Methodist Church on Elm Street. The bride will wear a white gown embroidered with pearls which probably cost a hell of a lot of... groom is a nativ...

MEANWHILE, 400 MILES AWAY...

WHERE IS THIS PARTY ANYW—*hic!* —ANYWAY?

763 BOTTLES OF BOCK ON THE WALL, 763...

BACK IN BUSTED BOWELS, SIGNS THAT ALL IS NOT WELL SLOWLY MANIFEST THEMSELVES

FUNNY...JASPER OUGHT TO BE AT HOME THIS TIME OF NIGHT.

BRR BRR

DONNA! HAVE YOU SEEN STEVE?

WHILE VERY FAR AWAY—

SAY—*hiccup!* —SHTEVE! THIS IS BIG BEND!

GEE, JASPER— IT SURE IS! I SHOULDA MADE A LEFT AT THAT DEAD ARMADILLO!

AWAKE AND SOBER, JASPER SUDDENLY REALIZES WHERE STEVE HAS BROUGHT HIM.

GEE, JASPER, I DON'T KNOW **HOW** WE MANAGED TO...

LET'S CAN THE POOP, STEVE-O.

I'VE KNOWN THAT SOMETHIN'S BIN HANKERIN' YOU FER SOME TIME. I **KNOW** YOU BROUGHT ME OUT HERE ON PURPOSE!

AND I KNOW YA DON'T COTTON TA ME MARRYIN' YER SISTER, NEITHER. YOU JUS' THINK I WANNA STEAL YER GRANDMA'S OIL, AND YOU WANNA **SHOW-DOWN!** WELL, STEVE-O, YOU GOT ONE!

WOW! HAVE I BEEN **THAT** OBVIOUS THIS WHOLE TIME?

FELLERS AS STUPID AS YOU USUALLY ARE!

AT LAST, STEVE GETS IT ALL OFF HIS CHEST.

OKAY, JASPER! I'LL LEVEL WITH YA! I GOT QUESTIONS ALL RIGHT!

HOW WERE YOU GONNA SELL THE LAND, JASPER? A SECRET DEAL WITH THE SAUDIS?

WHAT "SWEET NOTHINGS" DID YOU BRAINWASH MY BABY SISTER WITH, YOU STUNTED LITTLE PIP-SQUEAK LAB ACCIDENT? HUH!?

SHAKE SHAKE SHAKE SHAKE SHAKE SHAKE SHAKE SHAKE SHAKE SHAKE

ANSWERS! THAT'S WHAT I WANT!

A NICE OLD-FASHIONED TEXAS DUEL SEEMS TA BE IN THE MAKING HERE.

DID YOU SAY SOMETHING?

HMM? NO.

I WAS JUST THINK-ING... YOU'RE A REAL SWEET GUY... NOT LIKE OTHER GUYS I USED TO KNOW.

I WON'T ASK.

THANKS.

BACK HOME—

ARNIE, IT WAS A WONDERFUL WEEK-END!

SURE YOU DON'T NEED A RIDE TO WORK?

I'M SURE. I'LL CALL YOU.

SMEK

YES, IT LOOKS AS IF TRUE LOVE HAS ENTERED ARNIE'S LIFE AT LAST.

INDEED, YOU MAY ASK YOUR-SELF, "WHAT CAN POSSIBLY GO WR—?"

SHUT THE ✳@#!!✳ UP!

55

BACK TO BIG BEND—WHERE STEVE HAS BEEN LISTENING TO JASPER'S SURPRISING LIFE STORY.

YOU'RE KIDDING! YOU'VE BEEN IN FOSTER HOMES—

SINCE I WAS FOUR. WHEN I GOT OUTA COLLEGE—

—AN' MAH INVESTMENT COMP'NY TOOK OFF, I MADE A POINT OF DONATIN' AS MUCH AS I COULD TO CHILD WELFARE PROGRAMS.

WOW.

BUT I STILL WASN'T NEVER REAL HAPPY—'TIL. I MET YER SISTER.

GOSH.

CAN I GO GET MARRIED NOW?

OO, YEAH, THAT'S TODAY, ISN'T IT.

YOU KNOW, JASPER I FEEL TERRIBLE ABOUT ALL THIS!

THAT'S GREAT, STEVE, BUT KIN WE HURRY BACK NOW? I GOTTA GIT MARRIED IN SIX HOURS.

NO, REALLY I'VE BEEN THINKING ABOUT THIS. MAYBE I AM TOO JUDGMENTAL!

DONNA'S 26. I OUGHT TO KNOW BY NOW SHE CAN MAKE THE RIGHT DECISIONS ABOUT HER OWN LIFE! I SHOULDN'T BE SO OVERPROTECTIVE.

I WAS WRONG, JASPER! YOU'RE NOT SUCH A SLEAZEBAG AFTER ALL!

THANK YOU, STEVE! KIN I GIT A COUPLE MORE SHOTS IN?

NO LONGER ENEMIES (FOR NOW), STEVE AND JASPER HIT THE ROAD—FAST.

DID YA FILL UP?

BOTH TANKS. LET'S SEE THAT MAP!

YOU POLECAT! YOU HAULED US A WAYS OUT HERE!

LOOK, I ALREADY APOLOGIZED! LET'S WORRY ABOUT GETTING BACK.

HELL, STEVE-O, WE'RE STILL GONNA HAFTA BREAK EV'RY LAW THERE IS IF'N WE WANNA GET BACK ON TIME!

YEAH, I KNOW. STATE, LOCAL, AND FEDERAL!

Busted Bowels

VAST EXPANSE OF NOTHINGNESS

BIG BEND

MORE LIKE PHYSICS, THERMODYNAMICS AND GRAVITY, I'D SAY.

DID YOU USE THE TOILET? I'M NOT STOPPING!

WEDDING BELLS RING IN BUSTED BOWELS. (YES HA HA VERY FUNNY)

HOWEVER, THE ABSENCE OF THE GROOM HAS NOT GONE UNNOTICED.

THERE'S NO ANSWER.

SEE? HE MUST BE ON HIS WAY!

I DON'T KNOW IF WE CAN WAIT...

IN THE CHURCH SANCTUARY, SOME START TO GET A LITTLE CURIOUS.

"GREENSLEEVES" AGAIN!? THAT'S FOUR TIMES!

DON'T ASK ME! I JUST WORK HERE!

WHILE MILES AWAY...

HURRY, JASPER!

HOWDY. TWO MORNING SUITS, PLEASE. I'M IN A HURRY.

I'LL BET YOU ARE!

Clem's
WEST O' THE PECOS
FORMAL WEAR

EXT.—ALLEY—NIGHT
CHUCK WAITS ALONE, A BIT NERVOUSLY, IN THE DARKNESS.

GOD. **HOW** DID I GET INTO THIS?

I DUNNO—MAYBE I COULD JUST SPLIT AGAIN—LEAVE TOWN—THIS IS A LOT OF MONEY—I MIGHT BE ABLE TO FINANCE MY OWN FIRST FILM—

MAYBE I OUGHTA BREAK **INTO** THE MOVIE BUSINESS FIRST! **THEN** I CAN WORRY ABOUT MORAL DECAY!

PSST.

WHAT?

YOU CHUCK?

YEAH!

HEY, CALM DOWN, BUD! YOU GOT THE MONEY?

HERE!

ARE YOU OUT OF YOUR MIND!? DON'T FLASH THAT AROUND!

HEY, CHECK HIM OUT!

THAT WAS CLOSE. NOW, LISTEN, GEEK, THE STUFF'S IN THE THIRD TRASH CAN AT THE BACK OF THE ALLEY. —¡ADIOS!

JEEZ, HOW DOES A NICE MIDDLE-CLASS BOY LIKE ME GET MIXED UP IN CRUD LIKE THIS?

WELL, NOT TO WORRY, CHUCK. IT'S ALMOST—

ABOUT TIME YOU SHOWED UP! I WAS GETTIN' CRAMPS!

—OVER.

Erica & Arnie

YES, IT LOOKS LIKE LOVE, ALL RIGHT....

DOESN'T IT JUST MAKE YA WANNA POOP?

OH, COME ON, JOEY. IT'S BETTER THAN HAVIN' HIM THREATENING SUICIDE!

THAT'S JUST MY POINT! WHAT IF HE GETS IN OVER HIS HEAD, LIKE I DID? WHAT IF SHE **DUMPS** HIM!? HE'D **FREAK!**

WELL, I DON'T KNOW, JOEY. HE'S CHANGED A WHOLE LOT SINCE...

GUNTHER... THE BOY NEEDS OUR HELP, GUNTHER.

NOW WAIT JUST A COTTON-PICKIN' MINUTE...

GO AWAY, JOEY. I'M NOT LISTENING TO THIS.
GUNTHER! YOU'RE THE ONE MAKING A BIG DEAL OUT OF THIS!
The SHAFT Apartments
JOEY, RIGHT NOW IT'D BE **TOTALLY** INAPPROPRIATE FOR US TO "TAKE ARNIE OUT!"
THAT'S FINE TALK COMING FROM THE GUY WHO TOOK **ME** TO EVERY BAR IN TOWN WHEN I MET MONICA.
THAT WAS DIFFERENT! YOU NEEDED IT! YOU'RE A MORON!
WILL YOU TELL ME **WHAT'S** SO TERRIBLE ABOUT TAKIN' ARNIE OUT FOR A NIGHT WITH THE BOYS!?
YOU JUST WANT TO GO TO A TOPLESS BAR AND YOU'RE SCARED TO GO BY YOURSELF.
NO!
AND SO, THAT NIGHT...
WELL, HEY, ARN. WE'RE GLAD YOU COULD COME OUT WITH US!
OH, SURE. ERICA HAD TO WORK TONIGHT ANYWAY.
I GUESS YOU TWO ARE PRETTY MUCH AN ITEM, HUH?
PRETTY MUCH.
AW, SHE WON'T MIND YOU GOIN' OUT WITH THE BOYS, WILL SHE?
IS THIS WHERE WE'RE GOING? "THE MOUNTAIN OF VENUS"?
THE ONE 'N ONLY!
IS THIS, LIKE, A STRIP JOINT?
I'M AFRAID SO, ARNIE.
JEEZ, YOU GUYS ARE WUSSIES!
JOEY, WHAT IF WE CAN'T GET—
RELAX!
I NEED TO SEE SOME I.D.'s, GENTLEMEN.
-ulp- OKAY....
THANK YOU.
OF PUBIC SAFETY
TIN, TEXAS
LICENSE NUMBER 5484875
RESTRICTION A
EXPIRES 1989
DPS AUDIT NO. 459874651
NGWANG, MARTIN
8 WINDY PINES DR
USTIN, TX 78777
RADIATION SICKNESS.
TRY AGAIN.
SORRY, GUYS. I CAN'T LET YOU IN WITHOUT PROPER— **JOEY!!**
YOU KNOW EACH OTHER?
HEY, KEVIN! YEAH, HE'S IN MY CALC CLASS! HE'LL LET US IN.
WHAT MAKES YOU SO SURE OF THAT, WISEGUY?
BECAUSE I'LL DROP BY DOC BROWNLOWS OFFICE AND SHOW HIM THE XEROX COPY OF THE FINAL YOU SOLD ME THE OTHER DAY.
SMOKING OR NON-SMOKING?
JUST GIVE US A GOOD VIEW, KEV.

INSIDE "THE MOUNTAIN OF VENUS" CLUB.

HOLY MACKEREL!

MAN, IS SHE SOMETHING!? GO ON UP AND PUT A DOLLAR IN HER G-STRING, ARNIE!

JOEY!

GEE, I DON'T KNOW—

COME ON, ARNIE! WE'RE JUST OUT HAVIN' A LITTLE FUN! IT DOESN'T MEAN A THING! ERICA WON'T DUMP YOU FOR IT!

SEE, GUNTHER? THERE HE GOES. HE'S LOOSENED UP. HE'S CHILL. HE'S HAVING FUN HE WON'T DO ANY-THING STU—

ARNIE, DON'T USE QUARTERS!

YIIEEK!!

CLINK CLINK

HEY, ARN, LOOSEN UP! WE JUST CAME TO HAVE A LITTLE FUN, RIGHT? NO HARM DONE!

—YAWN!— GUESS I'M KINDA READY TO GO. HOW ABOUT YOU, ARNIE?

#1 #2

YEAH, OKAY, I—

GO!? JESUS, WE ONLY JUST GOT HERE! LET'S AT LEAST STAY AND GET OUR COVER CHARGES WORTH!

I CAN'T BELIEVE Y'ALL ARE SO TENSE! IS THERE SOME CATASTROPHE COM-ING UP I DON'T KNOW ABOUT?

ERICA! ARNIE!

OOPS!

ARNIE! ...OH, MY GOD...

HEY, DUDE, JUST KEEP CALM!

LET GO OF ME, GUNTHER!

ARNIE, I... ARNIE! I CAN EXPLAIN...

ERICA, WHAT ARE YOU DOING UP THERE?

HEY, WHAT'S GOING ON?

ARNIE, GET DOWN! YOU CAN'T COME ON STAGE!!

DON'T TELL ME TO GET DOWN!! WHAT ARE YOU DOING HERE?

B-BUT... WHAT ARE YOU DOING HERE!?

ME!? THIS WAS JOEY'S IDEA!

WHOA, DUDE!

ARNIE! ARNIE, PLEASE! DON'T FREAK OUT AND MAKE A SCENE!

OKAY! OKAY! OKAY! I CAN HANDLE THIS! I'M AN OPEN-MIN-DED GUY!

ARNIE, I WAS GONNA TELL YOU, I SWEAR! YOU SEE, MY PARENTS QUIT SENDING ME MY MONEY!

ERICA... MY BABY IS A DANCER AT "THE MOUNTAIN OF VENUS"

PLEASE UNDERSTAND, ARNIE! IT'S JUST SO I CAN PAY MY WAY THROUGH SCHOOL!

YEAH, YEAH ...OKAY. SURE. UH, GEE, ERICA. THAT'S VERY IMPRESSIVE!

OH... giggle... THANKS, ARNIE.

WELL, ACTUALLY, I WAS COUNTING THE MONEY.

AND SO... SO ERICA! TELL ME SOMETHING ABOUT THIS FRIEND OF ARNIE'S!!

JOEY? WELL, HE'S—

I MEAN, IS HE, LIKE, YOUR AVERAGE UNDERSEXED COLLEGE MALE?

WELL—YEAH—PROBABLY.

GOOD.

SO I GUESS YOU'LL HAVE LOTS OF FUN MESSING WITH HIS MIND, HUH?

MIND?

BEFORE THE BIG DATE...

I'M NERVOUS, GUNTHER, WHY AM I SO NERVOUS?—QUICK, GIVE ME A PEP TALK.

WELL, JOEY, JUST BE GLAD YOU'RE NOT A PRAYING MANTIS.

WHAT?

WELL, THE FEMALE PRAYING MANTIS ALWAYS CONSUMMATES THE MATING ACT BY DISMEMBERING THE MALE WITH HER PINCERS AND EATING HIM.

SO YOU SEE, SOME GUYS *DO* HAVE IT WORSE.

THANKS. THANKS A LOT.

WHAT ARE FRIENDS FOR?

HI! YOU MUST BE JOEY! GIMME JUST A SEC, OKAY?

OH MY GOD!

ERICA! IF MAXINE CALLS, TELL HER I WON'T NEED A RIDE TO WORK TOMORROW!

BREATHING HEAVILY; HEART RATE INCREASING.

OKAY, NINA!

NINA! HOW DOES HE LOOK?

OOOH...COULD BE AN ENTERTAINING NIGHT!

I KNOW HOW YOU FEEL, FELLAS.

JUST STUDYIN'. WHAT ABOUT YOU, ARN?

WELL, I'M WORRYIN' ABOUT JOEY, FRANKLY.

I MEAN, DID HE HAVE ANY IDEA WHAT HE WAS GETTING INTO TONIGHT?

WELL, IT *WAS* YOUR IDEA FOR HIM TO ASK OUT ERICA'S ROOMMATE, ARNIE.

SIR? WE'RE CLOSING NOW... SIR...?

ZZZ

WELL, GOD, I DIDN'T THINK HE WAS *SERIOUS!* NINA ISN'T *LIKE* ERICA, GUNTHER!

COME ON, ARN. WHAT'S SHE GONNA DO? SPLIT ON HIM?

ONE FINE AFTERNOON, GUNTHER HAD A THOUGHT:

GOD, WHAT AM I DOING HERE? THIS IS SUMMER, FOR GOD'S SAKE!

WHICH LED HIM TO TAKE ALL THE NECESSARY STEPS...

DROPS

...TO PRESERVE WHAT WAS LEFT OF HIS CRUMBLING SANITY.

AAAHHHHH...

EASTERN

SO, WHERE ARE YOU GOING FOR VACATION, GUNTHER?

HOME! WHERE DID YOU THINK?

GATE 17

WELL, RIGHT. BUT WHERE'S HOME?

AFRICA.

GATE 17

AFRICA!?

I'M A RHINO, AREN'T I?

GATE 17

BUT YOU'RE NOT AN INTERNATIONAL STUDENT!

LOOK, ARE WE GONNA BORE EVERYBODY WITH MY $@#!!※ LIFE STORY HERE?

I WAS BORN IN AFRICA, YOU SEE, BUT MY FOLKS MOVED TO THE STATES WHEN I WAS THREE.

OH, OKAY.

WHEN MY DAD RETIRED A COUPLE OF YEARS AGO, THEY DECIDED TO MOVE BACK.

SO THIS IS REALLY LIKE MY FIRST TRIP.

I JUST HOPE JOEY CAN SURVIVE WITH ME GONE FOR TWO WEEKS.

THE APARTMENT! IT'S MINE! ALL MINE! MINE MINE MINE!

AND SO GUNTHER BEGAN HIS VOYAGE TO THE CONTINENT OF HIS BIRTH...

NORTH AMERI

EU

AFRIC

ALREADY THE TRIP IS A PLEASURABLE ONE, AFFORDING HOURS OF BLESSED, BLISSFUL RELAXATION...

EXCEPT FOR IN THE COCKPIT.

PASADENA?

YOU HEARD ME!

'Hepcats' inaccurate

I would like to complain in the most obnoxious possible way about the technical inaccuracies in today's 'Hepcats.'

Any idiot knows that opening an airplane hatch at 40,000 feet would result in a drop in cabin pressure that would send the entire plane dropping to the ground like a brick.

Please see to it that no such further mistakes of this kind are made.

B. J. Tylenol
Aerodynamics

Throw his butt out!

This is in response to B. J. Tylenol's snitty complaints about yesterday's "Hepcats."

Who cares if "Hepcats" is aerodynamically inaccurate? Comics follow their own rules, not anything so boring as the laws of physics, gravity, or anything else.

If Wile E. Coyote can swallow dynamite and live, then Martin Wagner can throw anyone out of a plane he wants to.

Chuck Jones
Comics history

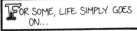

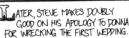

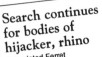

From *Exam Week Extra*, December 1987.

EARLY ON A LATE SUMMER'S MORNING... MEMORIAL SERVICES ARE ABOUT TO BEGIN FOR THE LATE GUNTHER RHINO.

THIS ISN'T REAL... IT ISN'T!

JOEY!

ERICA! GOD, I'M HAPPY TO SEE... HEY! WHERE'S ARNIE!?

HE'S GONE, JOEY! HE'S LEFT FOR AFRICA! HE WAS JUST SO OBSESSED!

HE'S GONE TO AFRICA!? HE'S CRAZY!

THAT'S NOT WHY I'M WORRIED! I MEAN, HE DID THIS SO FAST... JOEY, ARNIE'S NEVER BEEN ON A PLANE!

SIR? WE'VE LANDED NOW.

OKAY, COOL. THANKS.

AS GUNTHER'S MOURNERS FILE INTO THE LITTLE CHAPEL, FRANTIC THOUGHTS TROUBLE THE MINDS OF JOEY AND ERICA.

GOOD LUCK, ARN. PROVE THESE GUYS WRONG!

OH, ARNIE, BABY, PLEASE FIND GUNTHER ALIVE!

MEANWHILE, 6500 MILES AWAY...

WELL, THIS IS GONNA BE FUN!

FRIENDS, LOVED ONES, WE ARE GATHERED HERE TODAY TO REMEMBER GUNTHER, WHO...

NO-O!

JOEY!!

HE'S NOT DEAD! HE'S ALIVE! YOU HEAR ME! ALIVE! ALIVE!

HE'S FREAKIN' OUT!

JESUS!

NICE HYSTERICAL FIT, MR. BRANDO.

THANKS! I HOPE I GET A NICE BONUS!

LET US THROUGH!

OH GOD... MY HEAD...

WOW! I REALLY MUST HAVE MADE A SCENE BACK THERE, ERICA!

IT'S OKAY, JOEY. WE'RE ALMOST HOME.

WHAT'S THE USE? I GUESS GUNTHER'S DEAD AFTER ALL.

SHH! GO BACK TO SLEEP.

ELSEWHERE...

NOPE. NEVER SEEN HIM.

YOU SURE?

HEY, WE ALL LOOK ALIKE, DON'T WE?

WELL, ARN. SOME LUCK YOU'RE HAVING. SITTIN' IN SOME GRIMY RESTAURANT IN THE MIDDLE OF MALI...

A MILLION RHINOS... CAN'T FIND GUNTHER AMONG ANY OF 'EM... OF *COURSE*! AUTHORITIES WON'T TELL ME A THING, WHERE HIS FAMILY LIVES... SHOULD'VE STAYED HOME...

YEP... SHOULD'VE STAYED HOME.

MEANWHILE, BACK HOME...

OH...UH... AM I AT THE RIGHT PLACE?

FOR THE ROOMMATE AD? YEAH! COME ON IN!

DAYS LATER, AT JOEY'S APARTMENT.

MY GOD, JOEY! YOU SOLD *ALL* OF GUNTHER'S STUFF?!

ERICA, LISTEN...

BUT JOEY...

ERICA, YOU WERE RIGHT! I HAVE TO LEARN TO ACCEPT THE FACT THAT... WELL, GUNTHER IS DEAD. I HAVE TO LET LIFE GO ON.

I'M PLACING ADS AROUND FOR A NEW ROOMMATE

"WANTED: NON-SMOKING FEMALE TO SHARE 2-BDRM 1-BATH..." JOEY!

HEY, IT'S WHAT HE WOULD HAVE WANTED!

WELL, IT'S SURE AS HELL WHAT YOU'VE ALWAYS WANTED!

BACK IN AFRICA...

OH, WELL, I GOT A COUPLE DAYS TILL I FLY HOME. MAYBE I'LL GO TALK TO THAT YOYO AT THE EMBASSY AGAIN, AND...

!

GUNTHER!!!

OHMIGOD! IT'S GUNTHER! I KNOW IT IS! BUT HOW CAN I—?

OOF!

SORRY! 'SCUSE ME!

HEY!

YO! GUNTHER!

GUNTH! WAIT!

SLAM

77

WHAT IS THIS PLACE? LOOKS KINDA LIKE THE BACK OF A SHOP OR SOMETHIN'.

WELL, MAYBE I WAS WRONG. MAYBE IT WASN'T GUNTHER.

I'M GETTING RAGGED OUT... MY BRAIN IS FRIED.

STILL, SOMETHIN' ABOUT THAT GUY...

GOTTA CALM DOWN...

AH, WHAT THE HELL...

BAM BAM BAM

NOPE. WASN'T GUNTHER.

YEAH! THIS IS THE GUY WHO WAS FOLLOWIN' ME!

LOOK! IS AMERICAN PASSPORT!

YOU'RE OFF YOUR TURF, AMERICAN!

UH—

YEAH! NOW WHAT'RE YOU DOING FOLLOWING ME?

I WAS JUST LOOKING FOR A FRIEND—A-A RHINO, NAMED GUNTHER!

YOU KNOW GUNTHER!?

WOW! Y-YOU MEAN YOU'RE A FRIEND OF HIS TOO!?

BETTER THAN THAT! I'M HIS BROTHER, GOPHER!

"GOPHER"??

HEY, BRING GUNTHER'S FRIEND SOMETHING TO DRINK!

SO YOU KNOW GUNTHER, HUH? WELL, HOW IS THAT OLD HORN-HEAD?

UH... YOU MEAN YOU HAVEN'T HEARD?

HEARD WHAT?

WELL... UH... HE'S, UH, HE'S DEAD.

DEAD!? GUNTHER? REALLY?

YEAH. THERE WAS A HIJACKING AND ONE OF THE TERRORISTS PUSHED HIM OUT OF THE PLANE.

HMPH. WELL, GUNTHER NEVER **COULD** KEEP HIS STUPID BUTT OUT OF TROUBLE.

I TAKE IT YOU GUYS WERE PRETTY CLOSE, HUH.

ARNIE HAS MET GUNTHER'S BROTHER WHILE IN AFRICA...

LISTEN, AH, GOPHER... I WANT YOU TO TELL ME ONE THING.

WHAT ARE YOU GUYS **DOING** BACK HERE? WHAT'S WITH ALL THE GUNS AND THE SECRECY?

OH... WELL, I SUPPOSE IT WOULDN'T HURT IF **YOU** KNEW.

"BIKO" BY PETER GABRIEL?

WE SMUGGLE WESTERN ROCK RECORDS TO THE PEOPLE OF SOUTH AFRICA.

HANG ON. I'M NOT SURE HOW I SHOULD FEEL ABOUT THAT.

DIG IT, MAN! THEY **LOVE** THE SUPPORT!

OH, WELL. I GUESS I'VE BEEN ON A WILD GOOSE CHASE ALL ALONG.

I KNOW YOU PROBABLY THINK I'M TAKING GUNTHER'S DEATH LIGHTLY, ARN. IT'LL TAKE TIME TO HIT ME, THAT'S ALL.

WELL, GOOD LUCK WITH THE ANTI-APARTHEID CRUSADE, GOPHER.

THANKS! YOU WOULDN'T BELIEVE HOW HOT ROCK ACTIVISM IS, MAN!

YEAH, AND WE GET THE MUSIC TO THE PEOPLE WHO **NEED** IT!

SO YOU HAVE LIKE A WORLDWIDE OPERATION?

NOT AS SUCH, NO...

BUSINESS IS SLOW IN SOME PARTS...

YEAH?

YEAH, WE HAD 25,000 BILLY JOEL BOOTLEGS GOING INTO MOSCOW...

THEN THE SON OF A BITCH PLAYED A GIG THERE!

AND SO ARNIE FINALLY HEADED FOR HOME...

WELL, SO LONG, BUD.

IT AIN'T GONNA BE THE SAME AROUND HERE WITHOUT YOU.

WHILE ARNIE WAS SEARCHING THROUGHOUT AFRICA... JOEY'S THOUGHTS WERE OCCUPIED WITH SOMETHING OTHER THAN GUNTHER'S DEMISE.....

CHRIST! EVERY SINGLE CLASS AT THIS UNIVERSITY IS FILLED! EVEN THE **STUPID** ONES!

LATE LATE LATE REGISTRATION ←

HI! YOU LOOK PRETTY STRESSED OUT, DUDE!

THANKS FOR THE ANALYSIS! LOOK, FIND ME A CLASS, WILL YA!? ANYTHING!

WELL, THERE'S AN OPENING HERE, BUT IT'S...

I'LL TAKE IT!

BACK AT ERICA'S APARTMENT.

COME ON, ARNIE! SITTING AROUND MOPING ISN'T GOING TO DO YOU A BIT OF GOOD!

I KNOW. I JUST WISH I HADN'T FREAKED OUT SO MUCH WHEN I HEARD ABOUT GUNTHER'S DEATH. THAT WHOLE TRIP WAS A WASTE!

NO IT WASN'T!

IT WAS A VERY NOBLE THING TO DO.

EASY FOR YOU TO SAY! I OWE YOU 950 BUCKS!

HMM! WELL, MAYBE I CAN JUST TAKE IT OUT OF YOUR **HIDE**!

I, UH, YEAH... MAYBE YOU CAN!

Row 1:

Erica works on her tan between classes...

JEEZ. I CAN'T CONCENTRATE ON THIS STUFF ON A DAY LIKE THIS...

YEAH, THIS IS MORE LIKE IT... JUST BASKING IN THE SUN...

JUST BASKING... BASKING... MMM..

AAIIEE! SETTLE DOWN! I HAVEN'T EVEN OPENED THE BOTTLE YET!

Row 2:

ERICA CAN'T COME IN TONIGHT 'CAUSE SHE HAS A SUNBURN?

REALLY GUS, IT'S A MEAN ONE! SHE CAN BARELY MOVE.

OH, WELL. IS SHE GOING TO BE OKAY? NOT GONNA DIE OF MELANOMA ON ME?

NAH!

WHAT'S SHE DOIN' NOW? TAKIN' A NAP?

YEAH. SHE'S JUST TAKING IT EASY— READING SOME MAGAZINES.

Women face new cancer risks
"If the skin doesn't go, the boobs will," warn doctors

COSMO

Row 3:

MEANWHILE, MILES AWAY AT THE HOME OF RORY AND JUDY McLYON, ANOTHER PHONE CONVERSATION IS TAKING PLACE...

STEVE! STEVE GOLD! IT'S RORY! GUESS WHAT!? I JUST SOLD MY NOVEL!

REALLY!? RORY THAT'S TERRIFIC! SO HOW MUCH DID YOU GET?

WELL, NEXT TO NOTHING. BUT IT'S A FIRST NOVEL. THOSE DON'T DO SO HOT— UNLESS THEY BECOME BESTSELLERS, YOU KNOW.

WELL, HEY, BUDDY YOU NEVER KNOW!

NAH! NOT THIS ONE, STEVE. DON'T BE SILLY... THAT'D BE LIKE JUDY GETTING PREGNANT AGAIN!

Elsewhere...

YOU OKAY?

I-I DON'T KNOW.

Luzby's speaks

Row 4:

NO DOUBT ABOUT IT, MRS. McLYON. YOU'VE HAD A PIGLET IN THE PEN FOR 2½ MONTHS! CONGRATS!

OH, GOD!

AW, I WOULDN'T WORRY. SURE, WITH A WOMAN YOUR AGE THERE CAN BE SOME DIFFICULTIES, BUT YOU'RE VERY HEALTHY, AND...

THAT'S NOT IT, DR. JEREMY!

MY PRIVATE PRACTICE IS GOING GREAT! JOEY WILL GRADUATE COLLEGE IN A FEW YEARS, MAYBE! HOW WILL HE REACT TO A SIBLING TWENTY YEARS YOUNGER?

DAMMIT, MY LIFE WAS JUST BEGINNING!

WELL, NOW SO IS SOMEBODY ELSE'S.

JUDY! YOU'RE HOME! I'VE GOT A BIG SURPRISE!

UH, SO DO I, I GUESS.

OKAY! YOURS FIRST!

OH, NO NO NO. YOURS, BY ALL MEANS!

TA-DAAH! A CONTRACT FROM SIMON AND SCHUSTER! THE BOOK IS SOLD, BABY!!!

RORY! THAT'S WONDERFUL!

OKAY, SO WHAT'S YOUR SURPRISE?

WELL, HERE —HINT #1. A BOX OF "PAMPERS." WHAT COULD WE POSSIBLY USE THESE THINGS FOR?

4:28 A.M. JOEY McLYON ANSWERS THE CALL OF NATURE.

⚡#@!!☺

HEY! KILL THAT LIGHT, WILLYA?

OH. SORRY.

! ! !

!

GUNTHER!

WHAT?

GUNTHER! MY GOD!! YOU'RE ALIVE!

QUIT YELLING, WILL YOU? I GOT A HELL OF A HEADACHE! GOD, I HAVEN'T SLEPT IN ABOUT 30 HOURS.

BUT—BUT— THE HIJACKING! WE ALL THOUGHT YOU WERE DEAD! ARNIE EVEN FLEW TO AFRICA TO—

WELL, I'VE BEEN TRYING TO CALL YOU, BUT THE LINE'S BEEN BUSY ALL THE TIME!

OH...

VCR FOR SALE

10-SPEED CHEAP!

THAT. WELL...

OH, WILL YOU REMIND ME TO BUY A NEW CHAIN FOR MY BIKE IN THE MORNING?

"GUNTHER, YOU GOTTA TELL ME! HOW DID YOU MAKE IT!?"

"CAN'T WE TALK IN THE MORNING, JOEY? I'M ABOUT TO PASS OUT."

"NAW, COME ON, MAN!"

"ALL RIGHT, ALL RIGHT, DAMN IT!"

YOU BASTARD!! YOU'VE RUINED MY WHOLE WEEK-END!!!

ARRG!

81

TURN LOOSE O' ME, MAN! CAN'T YOU SEE YOU'RE ABOUT TO BE RHINO JUICE!?

HA! WHAT ABOUT YOU, YOU YOYO? YOU MUSTA KNOWN **YOU'D** GET SUCKED RIGHT OUTTA THAT PLANE TOO!

THAT'S RIGHT, RHINO! BUT I GOT MY SPECIAL PARACHUTE FROM MY "ISLAMIC JIHAD BOY-SCOUT TERRORIST PARTY-PAK"!

OH.

SEE!? THIS WAY I GET TO BE A MARTYR WITHOUT ACTUALLY DYING!

THAT'S NOBLE.

IF ONLY I CAN REMEMBER HOW TO WORK IT!

HA HA HA!!

"AT THAT POINT I KNEW I STILL HAD A CHANCE. BUT I WAS GOING TO HAVE TO MOVE FAST!

GIMME THAT!

POW!

WOMP!

OOF!

YOU KNOW I DEPLORE SENSELESS VIOLENCE, BUT I GOT MY LIMITS!

GUNTHER TELLS JOEY THE STORY OF HIS SURVIVAL.

IT ALL HAPPENED SO QUICKLY. BUT I WAS FLOATING DOWN SAFELY TO THE GROUND!

"I CAME DOWN ON A WIDE OPEN STRETCH OF VELDT, WHERE I WAS FOUND BY ONE OF THOSE COINCIDENCES YOU COULD ONLY FIND IN A COMIC STRIP."

FLYING COACH AGAIN, EH, SON? THAT'S SENSIBLE.

HAR HAR, DAD! CUT ME DOWN, WILL YA?

"AFTER DAD PICKED ME UP, EVERYTHING BECAME SURPRISINGLY NORMAL."

NOW, DAD, I KNOW YOU'RE WONDERING WHAT I WAS DOING UP IN...

OH, WAIT 'TIL WE GET HOME, GUNTHER, SO YOU CAN TELL YOUR MOTHER!

HONEY! GUESS WHO'S DROPPED OUT OF THE SKY!

GUNTHER! MY BABY!

OHH, LOOK AT HIM, GUS! I KNEW HE WASN'T GOING TO BE EATING RIGHT! HE'S LOST A WHOLE POUND, I KNOW IT!

NOPE! NOTHING LIKE A MOTHER.

OH, GUNTHER! WHY HAVEN'T YOU CALLED US NINE TIMES A DAY LIKE YOUR POOR MOTHER ASKED YOU TO?

"IT WAS A WHILE BEFORE I COULD TELL MY FOLKS ABOUT THE HIJACKING. MOM, I THOUGHT, TOOK THE NEWS RATHER 'PREDICTABLY.'"

FAN

FAN FAN

"I SPENT THE NEXT COUPLE OF WEEKS SORTING THINGS OUT WITH THE AUTHORITIES, AND TRYING TO SORT THINGS OUT BACK HOME, TOO. LIKE I SAID, I COULDN'T REACH YOU."

SO LAST NIGHT I FINALLY FLEW IN. I WAS SO TIRED WHEN I GOT BACK I CRASHED RIGHT HERE.

THANK GOD. AT LEAST YOU DIDN'T TELL ME THIS WHOLE THING WAS A DREAM.

NAH. EVEN "GARFIELD" ISN'T *THAT* LAME.

OH, WELL. I MUST SAY I'M GLAD TO BE BACK.

OH, GOD! HOW'M I GONNA TELL HIM?

ANYWAY... yawn... GUESS I BETTER GO GET A DECENT NIGHTS SLEEP.

IT'S ALL GONE! I'VE SOLD EVERYTHING!

YAAWN! JESUS! I'M GONNA SLEEP TIL 3 IN THE AFTERNOON!

HIS BIKE! HIS T.V.! HIS VCR! HIS CD PLAY-ER! HIS WEIGHTS! HIS...

SEE YA IN THE MORNIN', JOEY.

NO!

WHY DON'T YOU, UH, LIVE IN HERE FOR A FEW, UH, MONTHS?!?

REALLY, GUNTH! DON'T GO IN THERE! LET ME—

WHAT ARE YOU TALKING A—

!

♪ OH, ♪ JO-EY!

UHH...YES, GUNTHER?

I WAS HOPING YOU COULD TELL ME WHERE ALL OF MY THINGS ARE.

TH-THINGS?! WHAT THINGS?

YOU KNOW. MY T.V., MY VCR, MY BIKE, MY WEIGHT SET, MY STEREO, MY FURNI-TURE, AND ALL OF MY CLOTHES. YOU HAVEN'T SEEN THEM, BY ANY CHANCE?

UH—

WHERE WERE YOU GOING JUST NOW?

220

NOW SOME OF YOU JUST MIGHT REMEMBER THE SURPRISING NEWS JOEY'S MOTHER JUDY RECEIVED ABOUT HER PREGNANCY.

IN MOST FAMILIES, NEWS OF A NEW ARRIVAL IS USUALLY CAUSE FOR CELEBRATION.

KRASH!

AFTER 20 YEARS, HOWEVER, SUCH NEWS IS RATHER, ER, UNEXPECTED...

YOU... YOU DID THIS TO ME...

JUDY! RELAX! COME ON! DEEP BREATHING EXERCISES!

AS DAYS GO BY, JUDY TRIES TO CALM HER TEMPER AND SORT OUT HER CONFUSION.

JEEZ, AM I JUST BEING SELFISH?

GOT A GREAT CAREER, A FINE SON, THE MOST WONDERFUL HUSBAND...

PRIVATE PROPERTY KEEP OUT

I SUPPOSE I SHOULD COUNT MY BLESSINGS.

RORY... LISTEN ...WOULD YOU BE ANGRY IF... OH, NEVER MIND.

zznf ...WHAT, JUDY?

WELL, IF...FOR SOME REASON I DECIDED NOT TO KEEP THE BABY.

LISTEN, THIS HAS CAUGHT US BOTH OFF GUARD, SO, WELL, WHATEVER YOU DECIDE, I'LL RESPECT THAT.

THANKS HONEY.

THEN AGAIN, THERE IS THE PROSPECT OF SEEING THE LOOK ON JOEY'S FACE AFTER WE'VE REDECORATED HIS ROOM.

RORY, NOT SURPRISINGLY, HAS THOUGHTS OF HIS OWN ABOUT THE PROSPECT OF RE-FATHERHOOD.

WOW. SO IT'S BEEN 20 YEARS, AND JUDY'S GONNA HAVE ANOTHER BABY.

WRITERS

YEAH, IT'S GONNA TAKE SOME GETTING USED TO...

MAN, I REMEMBER— SO LONG AGO—WHEN WE WERE JUST A YOUNG AND HAPPY COUPLE.

BEEP BEEP BEEP

DAMMIT, I JUST MADE A CASSEROLE!

RORY, I CAN'T HELP IT!

 early one morning after Gunther's return.

YAWN

SCRATCH SCRATCH

doc REMOTE

YIKES

I CAN JUST SEE THE COVER OF NEXT WEEK'S "TIME."

GUNTHER? WHAT THE HELL ARE YOU DOING?

GET AWAY FROM THE WINDOW, MAN! IT'S THE MEDIA! I SHOULDA SEEN THIS COMING!

AW, JEEZ! DON'T YOU WANNA BE A MEDIA CELEBRITY? COME ON, I'LL LET 'EM IN.

NO!

GET AWAY FROM THAT WINDOW!

ARRG!!

THE DAILY

Gunther: Hijack survivor a psycho-freak?

Associated Ferret

Gunther Rhino, who in recent weeks has become something of a celebrity following his miraculous survival of an airline hijacking, in which he was thrown from Northnorthwest Airlines Flight 648, seemed reticent towards reporters and even attacked his roommate yesterday morning.

Gunther spent most of the morning hiding under his bedsheets, only emerging to strangle his roommate, Joey McLyon, 20, after McLyon agreed to allow reporters into their apartment.

ARNIE!? ERICA? COULD YOU GUYS GET OVER HERE QUICK!?

YEAH, YEAH, I KNOW ABOUT THE NEWS, BUT IT'S GETTING OUT OF HAND!

MR GUNTHER, COULD YOU TELL US—

HOW LONG WERE YOU IN—

DID YOU REALLY KILL THE HIJACKER WHEN—

HOW DO YOU FEEL RIGHT NOW?

I WANNA BE ALONE!

TONIGHT WE'RE COMING TO YOU LIVE FROM THE APARTMENT OF GUNTHER RHINO, THE LOCAL COLLEGE STUDENT WHO SURVIVED A DRAMATIC AIRLINE HIJACKING THIS SUMMER!

FROM THE OUTSET IT HAS BEEN APPARENT THAT GUNTHER HAS NOT BEEN WILLING TO ADDRESS REPORTERS' PRYING AND PERSONAL QUESTIONS.

ONE MUST ASSUME THAT EMOTIONS INSIDE THE APARTMENT ARE REACHING A FEVER PITCH!

COOL! THAT WAS ME! DID YA SEE!?

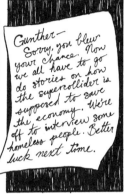

AND THE FOLLOWING NIGHT—

RORY! HURRY UP IN THERE! COME HELP ME PICK NAMES!

JUDY, YOU'VE BEEN PORING THROUGH THAT BOOK FOR DAYS!

YOU SHOULD READ IT! ITS GOT ABOUT A MILLION NAMES AND TELLS YOU WHAT THEY MEAN.

OH, YEAH? SO WHAT DOES "JUDY" MEAN? "BEACH BALL"?

HO HO HO. I THINK IT MEAN SOMETHING LIKE "HONOR THE LORD" OR SOMETHING.

HEY, LOOK UP 'RORY'!

OH, YES! HERE IT IS! "DOUBLE DELUXE JERKFACE."

"WITH FRIES." YOU FORGOT.

"HEPCATS' IS A WELTANSCHAUUNG OF ANIMALISM," SAYS THE INDEFATIGABLE L. DEAN WEBB.

H·E·P·C·A·T·S presents

True Confessions

#1,419

LOVE OVER a HOLIDAY WEEK-END

BRR BEE

ARNIE HAS NOT SPOKEN TO ERICA FOR 48 HOURS ...

KLIK

ARNIE HAS NOT SPOKEN TO ERICA FOR 48 HOURS AND 1 MIN—

SHUT UP!

CRASH

AIN'T LOVE SWEET, FOLKS? SURE IT IS.

TOMORROW: SOMETHING INTERESTING.

WEEKS PASS, AND PASS.

JUDY GETS PLUMPER AND PLUMPER.

ONE AFTERNOON, DURING A REGULAR OB-GYN VISIT...

I JUST CAN'T BELIEVE IT'S BEEN SIX MONTHS!

YOU DIDN'T HAVE AMNIOCENTESIS THE FIRST TIME OUT, DID YOU?

NO. JOEY WAS BORN... MY GOD ...1967!

IT'S ROUTINE STUFF. WE CAN PICK OUT THE BABY'S SEX FROM CHROMOSOMAL PATTERNS.

SO WHAT AM I SO WORRIED ABOUT? THIS PREGNANCY IS GONNA BE A PIECE OF CAKE!

HO-KAY. STEP ONE. DRINK THIS.

WATE H²O

"'HEPCATS' ANTICIPATES THE FUTURE OF ANTHROPOMORPHISM IN COMICS." — THE ERUDITE L. DEAN WEBB

91

NO, NOW REALLY JOEY. WE HAVE A LITTLE SUR—

WHERE'S MOM? I BET THIS IS ONE OF MOM'S STUPID JOKES!

MOTHER DEAR. WOULD YOU PLEASE TELL ME WHY THERE IS A CRIB, OF ALL THINGS, IN MY R—

DAAAD

IT'S OKAY, JOEY. HE KNOWS.

DAD?

YES, JOEY!

MOM'S P-PREGNANT, DAD!

YES, JOEY. SHE IS.

THIS ISN'T THE FIRST TIME, IS IT.

SADLY, NO.

A HEPCATS HOLIDAY RECAP: AS USUAL, CHRISTMAS OF '88 PROVED A MEANINGFUL GATHERING TIME FOR YOUNG LOVERS...

CUTE, ERICA. CUTE.

SORRY, BABY. THEY WERE OUT OF EXTRA-LARGE.

...EXPECTING PARENTS...

RORY, DID WE REMEMBER TO GET EACH OTHER ANYTHING?

HANG ON, I'M LOOKIN'.

...AND COLLEGE DORKS.

A LIFETIME SUBSCRIPTION TO PLAYBOY!? WOW! WHAT DID THIS COST!?!

I DUNNO. THEY'LL BE BILLING YOU IN INSTALLMENTS.

A HOLIDAY GATHERING AT THE McLYONS, WITH FRIENDS.

OW!

WHAT!?

IT'S THE BABY! WOW! SHE'S KICKING LIKE HELL.

WOW. CAN I FEEL HER?

JEEZ. IT'S BEEN SO LONG. I FORGOT...

HEY, Y'ALL!

ALL RIGHT, GUYS!

SOUNDS LIKE MORSE CODE, MOM.

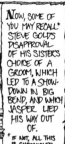

YOU OKAY, DAD? DAD?

YEAH. YEAH, GUESS I FLIPPED OUT FOR A SECOND THERE.

WOW. I NEVER THOUGHT I'D GET A BAD CASE OF THE THIRTYSOMETHINGS.

JUST SOME THINGS YOU THINK YOU'D LEARN, THATS ALL.

YOU KNOW, I'M REALLY LOOKING FORWARD TO THIS BABY! I MEAN, I'M...

DIG DIG

HERE, DAD. TAKE 'EM. I— I NEVER USE EM.

WHY SON— I-I DON'T KNOW WHAT TO SAY.

YOU KNOW, IN A LOT OF WAYS YOUR MOM'S NEW BABY WILL BE LIKE A FIRST BABY.

YOU MEAN 'CAUSE IT'S BEEN SO LONG?

YEAH, THAT. YOU'RE GONE, SO IT'LL BE THE PATTER OF LITTLE FEET ALL OVER AGAIN! AND YOUR MOM'S CAREER IS REAL SUCCESSFUL, TOO.

IS MOM REAL NERVOUS?

SHE KEEPS WORRYING HER WATERS GONNA BREAK IN THE MIDDLE OF A THERAPY SESSION.

JEEZ! SHE DOES HAVE IT BAD!

OH... MY... GOD....

MRS. McLYON?

JUDY!! WHAT IS IT!?

I-UH- SHE—

RITA, MY WATER JUST BROKE. DO ME A FAVOR AND CALL RORY, OKAY, RITA?

WHO THE HELL ARE YOU!?

DON'T YELL AT HIM, RITA. HE'S MY PATIENT.

DR. RENSHAW! CALL AN AMBULANCE! CALL EVERYBODY!!

...SHE YELLED AT MEEE...

IT'S OKAY, MR LEWIS. SHE DIDN'T MEAN IT. SIT DOWN, OKAY?

'CAUSE SHE'S HAVING A BABY, YOU ASSHOLE!

D-D-DOES THIS MEAN I GET A DISCOUNT ON TODAY'S SESSION?

NOOO PROBLEM.

JUDY'S BABY IS FINALLY ON ITS WAY.

OKAY, JUDY, YOU WANNA STAND UP, SIT DOWN, LIE DOWN, WHAT?

JEEZ. OH NO, I WAS A-FRAID THIS WAS GOING TO HAPPEN.

OW!— JUST— I NEED TO GET TO THE LADIES ROOM RIGHT NOW, THATS ALL.

LET ME HELP, OKAY? THEN I'LL GO CALL RORY.

YOU HAVEN'T CALLED RORY, YET? RITA, WHAT IN THE HELL HAVE YOU BEEN DOING THE LAST FIVE MINUTES!?

I WAS PANICKED, OKAY? I CALLED THE FIRST EMERGENCY NUMBER I FOUND.

YES?

I'M EARL TH' MAINTENENCE MAN. GOT A 'MERGENCY?

ANYWAY, MR. McLYON, YOUR WIFE HASN'T GONE INTO HEAVY LABOR, WHICH IS OKAY. WE'LL BE DELIVERING BY CAESAREAN SECTION.

THAT WON'T MEAN ANYTHING DIFFERENT FOR YOU. YOU'LL STILL GET TO CUT THE CORD AND EVERYTHING!

SORRY—SPACED OUT A SECOND THERE.

AW, HEY— WAIT TILL YOU SEE THE BILL FOR THIS.

THE BIRTH OF RORY & JUDY'S DAUGHTER COMMENCES.

OKAY, MRS. McLYON. TIME TO HAVE THAT BABY NOW!

MMN.

SAY, DOC, DO I HAVE TO SIT BACK HERE? I REALLY WANNA WATCH THIS!

HEH... WELL, A CAESAREAN'S PRETTY MESSY, MR. McLYON. BESIDES, YOU NEED TO BE GIVING YOUR WIFE ENCOURAGEMENT! WE DON'T WANT ANYTHING UNEXPECTED CROPPING UP.

OUTSIDE...

HI! I'M THE VIDEO GUY!

THE WHO?

I'M SORRY, SIR, I...

NO, IT'S OKAY, NURSE!... CHUCK!

HI, RORY.

JUDY & I AGREED THAT IF SHE EVER HAD A SECOND BABY WE'D LET CHUCK VIDEOTAPE IT. THAT'S OKAY, RIGHT?

UH... SURE.

I GOT HERE AS QUICK AS I COULD.

SO WHAT HAVE YOU BEEN DOING THESE LAST FEW MONTHS —LAST I HEARD YOU WERE SET UP ON SOME PHONY DRUG DEAL OR SOMETHIN'!

OH, THAT—WELL, MARTIN COULDN'T FIGURE HOW TO END THAT STORY SO...

HMM... TYPICAL.

PARDON ME. WE'RE **TRYING** TO HAVE A BIRTH HERE.

Judy, on the delivery table...

WOW...

THIS IS STRANGE...

I'M WIDE AWAKE BUT IT'S LIKE I'M

FLOATING

OR SOMETHING...

MY BABY...

IS SHE OUT YET?

YOU KNOW, RORY, I WAS THINKING...

YEAH?

MAYBE WHEN THIS IS ALL DONE, WE CAN EDIT THIS VIDEO TO A RECORD OR SOMETHING.

CHUCK! CHUCK'S HERE!

YOU MEAN LIKE A MUSIC VIDEO?

WHAT THE HELL?

OKAY. WHAT SONG?

I DUNNO. HOW 'BOUT "SHE'S HAVING A BABY?"

HOW ABOUT "HEAVY DUTY JUDY" BY FRANK ZAPPA?

BOY, YOU GUYS ARE HILARIOUS.

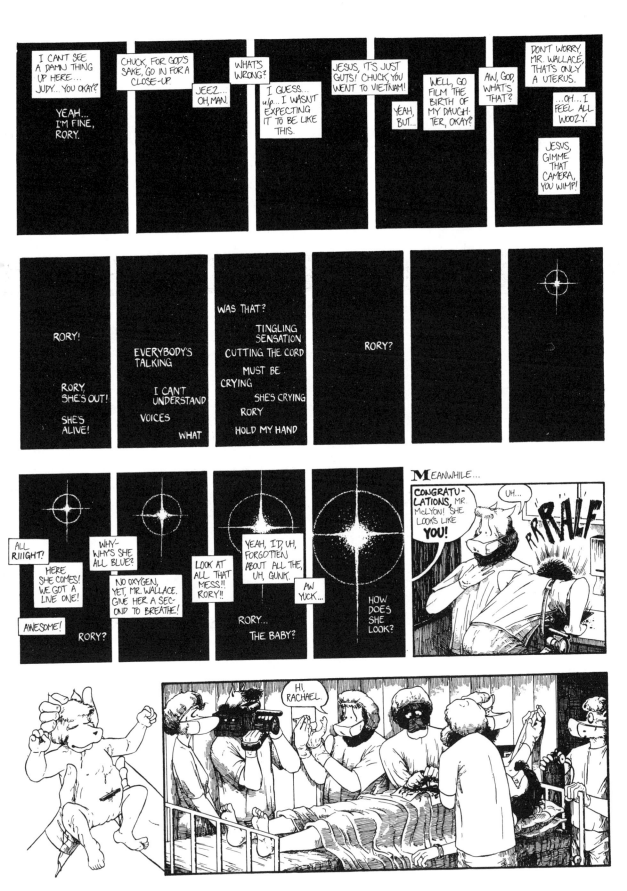

WELL, HI THERE, DAD. AND WHAT ARE YOU STARING AT?

ACK!
THIS IS A COMIC STRIP! *jiggle...*

JOEY McLYON, 21 YEARS AN ONLY CHILD, IS ABOUT TO LEARN WHAT IT MEANS TO BE A BIG BROTHER...

YEAH, FRIDAY NIGHT... YOU **WILL**? WOW!
I MEAN, UH, YEAH 8:30! RIGHT!

HANG ON JUST A SEC. I GOT SOMEONE ON THE OTHER LINE...

HI, BABY, IT'S MOM! LISTEN, I GOTTA COME UP TO TOWN FOR A CONFERENCE THIS WEEKEND.
CAN YOU BABYSIT RACHAEL FRIDAY NIGHT?

FOR GOD'S SAKE, MOM, WHY CAN'T YOU LEAVE RACHAEL WITH DAD?
HE'S OUT OF TOWN, TOO. I'M SORRY IF THIS IS INCONVENIENT, SWEETHEART. LOOK, I'LL PAY YOU 20 BUCKS.

JEEZ. THINK THINK THINK.
HANG ON A SEC, MOM.
click!
HEY BABE- STILL THERE? YEAH, JUST A SEC.

click! MOM? LISTEN, IT'S NO PROBLEM. BRING HER UP.
OH, THANKS, JOEY! THANKS A LOT!

HEY GUNTHER!
HEY WHAT?

GUNTHER! GUNTH, GUESS WHAT! YOU KNOW THAT THOROUGHLY AMAZING BABE IN MY GOVERNMENT CLASS? YOU KNOW?

SHE'S GONNA GO **OUT** WITH ME! IS THAT **GREAT**? THIS WEEKEND, TOO! FRIDAY NIGHT! GONNA GO EAT, GO DANCING...

SO... ahem... ANY- WAY... I WANTED... WELL, YOU KNOW... WOULD YOU, LIKE....

WHY, YES, JOEY, I'LL BE HAPPY TO BABYSIT YOUR SISTER FOR YOU.
AW, GUNTHER! YOU'RE A GOD AMONG RHINOS!

105

BACK AT ERICA'S APARTMENT...

SURE, I HEARD ABOUT THIS SUNDAY. YOU DON'T EXPECT **ME** TO DANCE... DO YOU?

YOU **BET** I DO. YOU'RE A DEEJAY. BESIDES, IT'S ONLY FAIR....

YEAH... B-BUT... **I'M** NO DANCER! I MEAN, I

ARNIE. SWEETHEART. YOU THINK **I** HAD PROFESSIONAL TRAINING WHEN I STARTED OR SOMETHING?

LISTEN, ERICA, LET'S TALK ABOUT THIS... I...

ERICA!

STOP...

MMMM...

DON'T TRY TO APPEAL TO MY BASE INSTINCTS, HONEY.

PLEASE?

I DON'T HAVE TO **TRY**, ARNIE.

Master

AND AFTER SOME DISCUSSION, ARNIE IS PERSUADED TO DANCE

UM, ERICA? YOU KNOW, I'M REALLY NOT READY FOR THIS...

I FIGURED THAT. SO I'LL GIVE YOU SOME POINTERS. CONSIDER THIS PRACTICE.

BUT—

BUT NOTHING. THIS IS A GOLDEN OPPORTUNITY FOR YOU TO SEE JUST WHAT I GET TO GO THROUGH EVERY NIGHT OF THE WEEK.

JEEZ, ERICA. I D.J FOR YOU. ISN'T THAT—

ARNIE, DEAR. I WANT MY TABLE DANCE... OR DO YOU WANT THIS MONTH'S RENT?

THAT WAS JUST A BIT TOO MUCH.

STRIP, BUCKO.

ERICA TALKED YOU INTO DANCING AT "THE MOUNTAIN OF VENUS"?! HOW?

IT WAS BLACKMAIL, GUNTH. PURE AND SIMPLE.

SAY WHY DON'T YOU DANCE? I BET ERICA COULD MAKE YOU A T-BACK.

HAH! ME?! GET REAL!

WHADDA YOU MEAN? YOU'RE BUILT! YOU'D WALK HOME WITH AT LEAST 150 BUCKS!

ARNE, IF I THOUGHT I COULD BE A CHIPPENDALES DORK I WOULD BE. BESIDES, WHAT'S A T-BACK ANYWAY?

YOU KNOW, WHAT YOU GOTTA WEAR ON STAGE. LIKE A G-STRING.

TRUST ME, ARN. THEY DON'T MAKE 'EM FOR GUYS LIKE ME.

IT'S "GUYS-DANCE" DAY AT THE MOUNTAIN OF VENUS.

GUNTHER! WHAT ARE YOU DOING HERE? ARE YOU DANCING?

ME!? HELL NO! THE GIRL WHO'S GONNA D.J ASKED ME TO BACK HER.

DRESSING ROOM

KELLY? YEAH, I THINK SHE'LL MAKE A GOOD D.J....

CHRIST ALMIGHTY! IS THIS WHAT YOU'RE WEARING!?

DRESSING ROOM

WELL, THAT'S JUST MY T-BACK. I'M...

HEY, WHY DON'T YOU WEAR THIS ONE WITH THE LITTLE SMILING HOT DOG ON FRONT?

DRESSING ROOM

⚡@#!!✳️ OFF!

BREAK A LEG, ARNIE!

DRESSING ROOM

THE DAY AFTER THE BIG DAY, AS GUNTHER STEADILY DECOMPRESSES, JOEY, IT SEEMS, IS JUST GETTING CRANKED UP.

GUNTH! I'M BACK!

WHAT'S ALL THAT FOR? WE ALREADY HAD A GRADUATION PARTY!

STUFF THAT CRAP! THIS IS YOUR "MOVING-OUT, STARTING-A-REAL-LIFE" PARTY! FROM ME TO YOU!

OH, FOR GOD'S SAKE, JOEY! YOU DIDN'T GO RENT A BUNCH OF PORNO MOVIES, DID YOU?

HA! I'LL HAVE YOU KNOW THIS IS SOPHIS-TICATED EROTIC ENTER-TAINMENT FOR DIS-CRIMINATING ADULTS!

YEAH, RIGHT.

HEY, YOU ONLY GRADUATE ONCE, RIGHT?

"YANK MY DOODLE."

ANOTHER DAY PASSES...

WOW. IT'S JUST STARTING TO HIT ME. IT'S OVER!

I'M NOT A STUDENT ANYMORE.

AND AT THE END OF THE WEEK, I'M MOVING OUT, GOING HOME FOR THE SUMMER...

BUT WHAT AM I GOING TO DO WITH MY LIFE?

MAYBE I CAN CATCH THE "BATMAN & ROBIN" FESTIVAL AT DOBIE!

AS GUNTHER BEGINS PREPARATIONS TO MOVE OUT, PACKING AWAY OVER FOUR YEARS OF HIS LIFE...

SO, JOEY, ARE YOU GONNA LOOK FOR A NEW ROOMMATE OR SOMETHING?

NAH.

I THINK I'M GOING TO LOOK FOR A ONE-BEDROOM EFFICIENCY, MAYBE CLOSER TO CAMPUS.

YOU!? LIVE ALONE!? YOU WON'T SURVIVE!

LAUNDRY GIVES YOU CONVULSIONS. YOU CAN'T COOK. YOU'RE NOT RICH ENOUGH TO EAT OUT EVERY DAY.

OH, KNOCK IT OFF. I CAN DO AS WELL AS ANY GUY MY AGE, AND ANY IDIOT CAN MICROWAVE.

BUT JOEY, YOU AREN'T JUST **ANY** IDIOT.

SEE THIS PIZZA? THIS PIZZA HAS LASTED ME A **WEEK**!

THE END.

Supplement
TO THE DAILY HEPCATS

As stated in the introduction, this supplement is meant to provide insight and background into the circumstances surrounding the creation of some of my *Hepcats* daily strips. Both series highs and lows are discussed here, and I also take the opportunity to explain a handful of failed gags. I hope you find this interesting, particularly if you are an aspiring cartoonist yourself, intrigued by the process of how something now established first came into being. If not, skip to the *Shasta Says* section. No hard feelings.

Page 10, strip 3
Yikes! Glom that early Gunther!

Page 12, strip 3
I took a psychology class in summer 1987 to fill a requirement and it was interesting as hell. To get full credit we had the choice of writing a paper (which nobody did), and being guinea pigs in experiments run by graduate students (which everybody did). This inspired this story, which, unlike the following video thing, was not taken *directly* from real life.

Page 15, strip 4
I really did direct a series of video scenes for therapist Judy Miller, the real-life Judy McLyon, in Houston in 1986. I still think they turned out well. Judy tells me she had great success using the videos at seminars in following years. Almost every strip in the story that follows is taken from actual incidents during actual shooting, sometimes right down to the exact dialogue. The party on page 21-22 really happened, too. I'm not sure if this is all that great a comic strip story, but I was still getting my legs on *Hepcats* at this phase. I had no idea who the principal characters were yet going to be, or which direction the strip would take. But, since my first semester was a summer one, and the readership was limited, I took my time.

Page 18, strip 2
I tried giving Joey a number of girlfriends but none of them worked out. It was a lot like real dating. In retrospect I'm surprised that, being so new to all of this, I let the stories tell themselves and they'd work out fine. Back when I was trying to write short fiction as a teenager I'd either overthink or underthink the plotting, and it would never work. Guess I found my element.

Page 19, strip 4
The octopus guy was just too weird. I stuck to mammals from then on.

Page 25, strip 3
I made few friends in the UT greek community with this story, and this strip in particular, and for the longest time *Hepcats* had an anti-frat reputation. I even got an anonymous nasty message on my answering machine.
 Fraternities at the University of Texas at Austin have the worst reputations of any frats in the country, which, when you

consider the competition, is pretty impressive. Virtually every conceivable impropriety ("atrocity" might be too loaded a word) has been attributed at one time or another to certain brotherhoods, and for a while they were almost universally condemned, a bit of an unfair, reactionary generalization, to be sure. But violent, humiliating hazing, though illegal, still goes on openly at some houses. This strip refers in an unsubtle way to a shameful incident at a frat in 1987 involving the alcohol poisoning death of a freshman pledge, and the curious, hush-hush behavior of the frat following the incident. The year after I left, race wars to rival Los Angeles came close to breaking out on campus in response to several incidents of flagrantly racist behavior almost bordering on violence that some frats had started. *Texas Monthly*, a major magazine, ran a feature in 1991 titled "Are UT Frats Out of Control?" The zany thing is, almost all these guys are Republicans!
 Many fratboys are cretins, but certainly not all. In fact, I made lots of friends at Chi Phi (who, I guess, were tickled I was slagging rival houses). I designed a T-shirt for a toga party they held and was given red carpet treatment at the party, a rowdy affair replete with food fights. No one was raped, killed, or arrested. I had a blast.

Pages 31-32, all strips
This story really tanked. First, Chuck's grey narration boxes were too wordy (I reworked them somewhat for *Yo;* these are the original versions). Secondly, the hyper-tight sequentiality rendered any reader who missed so much as one day of the paper hopelessly lost. I think it's a funny bit, but it only works when read all at once. We learn by doing.

Page 37, strip 3
Two Events, one major and one minor, in a single strip here. Megan (Meagan in real life) was the girl I should have married. She was sharp, independent, with clearly delineated goals in life and a bullshit threshold so low you could trip over it if you weren't looking. She was also a complete babe who let me draw a rose on her inner thigh on our first date (a *lunch* date), and the only woman whose bizarrely eclectic musical tastes matched mine almost note-for-note. So what happened? She chose a disastrous relationship with a loutish bassist for a local heavy metal band. Women are hard enough to figure out. Brilliant women can give you an aneurism. Ah, well. She and I are still good friends. She's currently living in Hokkaido, in northern Japan.
 And of course, the first appearance of Arnie, the Major

event. Real-life storytelling isn't like that which is all made-up. Major characters cannot be worked out in a single sitting. You'll try out many, some will stick around if they work for you and others won't. Count all of the major players in this book who have not graduated to the comic book and you'll see what I mean.

Page 39, strip 2-page 41, strip 2
This story was a big gamble from the outset. I was slightly nervous dealing with the concept of suicide (as recently as the spring 1993 semester a student shot himself in Jester dorm), but also giddy at the thought of pushing the envelope. About halfway through the thing two friends showed up at my room in Jester expressing genuine concern for my emotional well-being—was I trying to "reach out" through my comics? On the day the next to last strip ran—in the heat of finals week—five people called the *Texan* office to ask if Arnie had really done himself. Van Garrett fielded all the calls, poor fellow. He told me, "One guy sounded really upset." At the risk of sounding gooey and melodramatic, maybe I "reached out" to those five people, maybe defusing five high-voltage situations. Who knows?

Page 42, strip 1
I still did not have the chops to draw my characters to where differences in age were discernable. (Note also the proto-*Li'l Hepcats* stuff on page 67.) Compare my rendering of the supposedly middle-aged Judy here with that in *Hepcats* #10.

Page 47, strip 1
An English professor of Romany (Gypsy) descent went berserk over this one. I apologized for the unintended slight but, I fear, in my youthful glibness I suggested that it was just a joke and maybe he needed a better sense of humor. His response to my diplomatic lapse was as charitable as could be expected, and he sent an 'enormous packet of photocopied articles to me at the *Texan* office detailing the centuries of ethnic violence that Gypsies have endured. Sobering stuff. Properly chastised, I thanked him for the info and reiterated that I hadn't meant any racial slur, and that I never even knew Gypsies were a race until now. So, if any of you reading this are Gypsies, no offense, eh?

Page 49, strip 1
A favorite among women readers.

Page 50, strip 3
"Repeat as necessary." Along with "urine sample," probably everyone's favorite gag.

Page 51, strip 2
Everyone asks this, so I hope I can just say it once right here and put it to rest. I have no idea what kind of animal Erica is. I just made her up. In fact, I find it surprising people consider this such an important thing to know—though, as I learned when I began to encounter "furry fans," as they like to be called, for the first time, species delineation is an important tradition in the eyes of fans. *Hepcats* set a startling precedent for furry comics, in that I was writing about realistic characters for whom the particular choice of species was not as important as the personalities. This

untraditional approach threw some longtime anthropomorphic traditionalists off-kilter.

Page 54, strip 4-page 55, strip 4
I swear I wasn't aware of all this sexual symbolism in the art while I was doing these strips. I just wanted to have some elaborate, peaceful forest scenes leading up to the idyllic panel with the two lovebirds nestled in each other's arms. Chris Ware said he couldn't take his eyes off the diagonally jutting tree trunk in strip 2, page 55. Van Garrett's comment: "Those aren't campin' grins!" Also, a couple of women I knew reported their boyfriends were a bit steamed, thinking I was referring to a secret tryst with their ladies. Surreal. In all, this week went over big.

Page 64, strip 3
Chris Ware pointed out that I seemed to have a real fascination with the news media and the way in which it presents and/or distorts things to the public. Yes, I suppose, but primarily I am fascinated by the phenomenon of the small town newspaper, many of which I am exposed to due to my parents' retirement to deep east Texas. It is refreshing for us city dwellers to remember that, in our light-speed, head-exploding information age, there are still little areas of America where high school cheerleader tryouts and church picnics are front page news.

Page 72, strip 1
A student and fan named Michael Sciascia wrote a letter to "Firing Line" parodying the style of the "B. J. Tylenol" letter and going into detail about just how wrong B. J. was, which is true. One point Mr. Sciascia made was that airplane doors open inwards (partially true—they "pop" inwards then swing outwards), which would prevent the terrorist from opening it at all. I tend to brush stuff like this off, and in fact Mr. Sciascia showed up at my University Co-op signing and confessed it had all been meant in good fun, which I figured. (You'd have to be majorly lacking a life to take a comic strip *that* seriously.) I drew a crashing airplane in his copy of *Yo*. Much of the point of the gag is, of course, that most people who write frothing letters to the editor couldn't find their ass with both hands and a compass. Not including Mr. Sciascia, of course.

Psge 76, strip 2
Not, of course, intended as an "all blacks look alike" racial gag. They're all rhinos, you see. You sometimes walk a fine line in this biz.

Page 78, strip 4-page 79, strip 1
No one got this rock activism stuff. There's a distinct danger in putting your personal passions into your own work and expecting them to be understood.

Page 80, strips 1 & 2
My only case of self-plagiarism, which did not turn out nearly as well as the original *Shasta Says* versions. I never did it again. A perfect example of how my interest was slipping in this semester.

Page 84, strip 4
So's this.

Page 90, strips 2 & 3

This is about as desperate as I got. Thankfully it was uphill from here.

Page 90, strip 4

Judy Miller, the real-life model for Judy McLyon, had Rachael, her first child, in late 1988—I think. During the latter part of her pregnancy I began asking for as much info as I could on how the process was going—amniocentesis, c-section, the works. She knew what I was up to but let me in on it all the same. What a trooper!

Page 94, strip 1

The asterisked comment here refers to the most frustrating and hurtful episode I endured at the *Texan*, specifically, the paper's refusal to acknowledge the publication of *Yo: The First Hepcats Book* in any way, shape, or form. The publication of *Yo* was a very exciting event for me, and upon its release I approached the Entertainment editor to see if they might like to do a little piece about it. Nothing major, just a sidebar on how I got the book together. The grounds for refusal were given as "conflict of interest," probably true in a pedantic sense, but my point of view was, "This isn't *The New York Times*, so who really cares?" Well, apparently, the board of Texas Student Publications cared, since they do seem to think the *Texan* is the *Times* (or, at least, *The Austin American-Statesman Jr.*), and therefore, a report on the private publication of a book by a *Texan* staff member was conflict of interest and out of the question. I pointed out that the *Texan's* "weekend entertainment supplement," *Images*, had not only done a full-page feature on the Eclipse publication of Chris Ware's *Floyd Farland: citizen of the future*, but that Chris' debut in *Raw Vol. 2 No. 2* had earned the *Images* cover. The editor shook off this double standard as irrelevant and I was left out in the cold looking bewildered.

Understanding of this unfriendly situation requires a deeper explanation of the poisonous atmosphere redolent at the *Texan*. Despite the often boisterous parties, the *Texan* in the late 80s was as cutthroat as PTL in the Bakker years. There were two ways you could become a staff pariah. One, by not being a member of the accepted cliques, and two, by excelling in your line of work beyond the current level of your colleagues, which fanned more jealousy than the average Homecoming Queen pageant. The only way to avoid number two was to excel in such a way that reflected favorably upon the paper as a whole. Thus, Chris Ware's publication in the highbrow, Penguin Books edition of *Raw* was acceptable to publicize, since the *Texan* could go, "See, look what wonderful things have happened to one of our own. A big New York publisher has released his work!" On the other hand, a student spitting on his hands, grabbing a pick and shovel, and putting something out with his own efforts, money, and hard work was, I guess, thoroughly unimpressive and not really worth the space. (Another reason for favoritism towards Ware was that his work was brilliant, artistically stunning, and over the heads of virtually every student, whereas *Hepcats* and Van Garrett's *Burnt Orange Blues* were accessible and popular, like TV sitcoms. It was certainly none of Chris' doing. Chris is perhaps the most egoless working cartoonist I have ever had the privilege of being involved with. But this newspaper swore by the cliché that art and popularity are mutually

exclusive.) Anytime that I would try to sneak a remark about *Yo* into the strip, the managing editor would chomp on my ass like a drill sergeant.

If this sounds to any of you like five-year-old sour grapes all I can say is that you really should work one semester for the *Texan*. Just one semester. If you survive without going up on a homicide charge you'll at least see where I'm coming from. (Hey, at least I was never summarily fired at a moment's notice, like many other cartoonists.)

Recently, much of the ill-feeling I've harbored passed when I learned that the aforementioned Entertainment editor is now holding down a shit job at the *Statesman*. I'm travelling the country and signing autographs. Hee hee hee. Ain't I a stinker?

Page 96, strip 1

Joey's handing his dad a string of condoms here. Most people missed this.

Page 98, strip 4–page 99, strip 4

The visual inspiration for this bit came from the "Abhorring Vacuums" chapter of *Cerebus: Church & State Volume II*. I guess I was looking for a way to delicately depict childbirth. For some reason, at this stage of my run, it seemed virtually everything I was doing was being mercilessly lampooned by Van Garrett, and as you can imagine this sequence came in for particularly uproarious clobbering.

Page 100, strips 1–3

Lest anyone gets the wrong impression: I think babies and kids are okay as long as they're someone else's. This bit was based on observation, not personal experience. Just so you'll know.

Page 105, strip 4

Such an event really happened on a Sunday afternoon at Tif's club. Not only male employees but boyfriends as well were being hit over the head and carried off to participate. I'm proud to say I wimped out thoroughly.

Page 111, strip 1

A brief note here for continuity maniacs. Obviously there are inconsistencies between the continuity of the daily strip and the comic book. The restructuring of *Hepcats* into a longer, more naturalistic narrative sort of thing has necessitated a few alterations right down to the DNA code. For example, the *Snowblind* graphic novel obviously takes place before Gunther graduates and he and Joey quit living together, but the climax of *Snowblind*, as we will see, means events cannot have taken place quite as depicted here. Part of my justification for the malleability of the *Hepcats* continuity as it relates to the Joey/Gunther/Arnie/Erica nexus (the other characters don't play a major part in the comic book, as many of you know), is that the daily strip was my training ground, and my radical shift towards a whole different kind of comic storytelling in a sense gave me a clean slate to work from. In other words, "Okay, I've got it now, these are the characters, this is what their lives are...NOW...here's number one." Nevertheless, the daily strip is a crucial part of *Hepcats* history and discrepancies cannot be dismissed. Here, therefore, for those of you into that sort of thing, is my modified timeline for *Hepcats* events as they currently stand, compromising daily strip and comic book continuities. Note these dates do not necessarily corroborate to the dates on which these stories were drawn.

- August 1985: Joey and Gunther move into Jester and start college. (*The Freshman Quintet.*)
- April 1986: *Hepcats* #1.
- June 1986: Joey falls in love with Monica. (Daily strip.)
- September 1986: Joey and Gunther, slow movers, pledge to a frat. (Daily strip.)
- November 1986: Joey meets Arnie. (Daily strip)
- December 1986: Arnie fakes suicide attempt. (Daily strip.)
- March 1987: Arnie meets Erica. (Daily strip.)
- May 1987: Arnie learns Erica's a stripper. (Daily strip.)
- February 1988: Everybody goes to Mardi Gras in New Orleans. (*Hepcats* #2: "Trial by Intimacy")
- June-August 1988: Gunther's bizarre odyssey back to Africa. (Daily strip.)
- September 1988: Joey's sister Rachael born. (Daily strip, date pushed back.)
- October 1988: Arnie gets brief job as DJ at Erica's club. (Daily strip.)
- December 1988-March 1989: *Snowblind.*
- May 1989: Gunther graduates.

For now, we'll stop there. You'll notice a couple of major changes, such as pushing Rachael's birth back from Christmas 1988, as it's depicted in the daily strip, to early fall. Thinking of the comic book as a full child to the daily strip's fetus may help, but, if you're the kind to let minor alterations like this get under your skin, remember, it's my party and I'll flake if I want to.

A Beginner's Guide

TO SHASTA SAYS

I consider *Shasta Says* the real kickoff point of my cartooning career. Though I still had ambitions of being a filmmaker at this age (20), and though I was not paid for the work at all in the first semester, there was no turning back from this point on. People who kept up with this strip often suggested I should try for syndication. No, I said, being a cartoonist is no way to make a living. But whether I liked it or not, I was going to be a cartoonist. And it's still no way to make a living.

Shasta Says differed from *Hepcats* in several ways. First, there was a stronger *Doonesbury* influence in that the humor was almost all issues-oriented. Whatever the hot topic on campus was that week, that's what I would lampoon. *Shasta Says* had no regular cast of characters (and everybody pretty much looks like Joey), though the *Cougar* staff appeared in several continuing stories, including a long one I've omitted here about a staff reporter being sent to a Soviet gulag for supposedly spying.

Looking over these strips for the first time in six years, I still find many of them delightful and funny, though of course much of this feeling is heightened by nostalgia. (One thing that does crack me up is just how dated all this "Hey, dude!" slang sounds already.) This early work is often crude but, I think, imbued with the same sense of naive elegance that makes the early *Cerebus*, *Academia Waltz*, or *Doonesbury* still appealing. The young man who produced these strips was high on life and just as full of himself. Occasionally he makes me cringe, but I'm still kind of proud of him.

The strips I have chosen to run here are hopefully presented in such a way to avoid the "I guess you had to be there" syndrome. I'm sure that there may still be some references you just won't get, but with any luck they're minimal. For the sake of clarity, I will explain a few things. (By the way, four other *Shasta Says* strips that do not appear here, including the very first one, can be seen on page 32 of *Hepcats* #5.)

Shasta was the name of the cougar who was the UH mascot. She was a beautiful animal, and she lived in a rather uncomfortable-looking pen right there on campus by the Cullen administration building. Every day before classes I'd make it a point to go and just sit by her cage for a while, talking to her and picking up cool feline vibes. One thing I wish I'd managed to get into was the Cougar Guard, a group of students who looked after Shasta, feeding her, acting as her handlers at football games, and actually taking her for walks on the UH campus while a flunky ran ahead and scattered students with the alert "Cougar coming through!" One day, I'll get back down to the UH campus, stroll the leaf-strewn pathways to Shasta's cage, and she and I will do some catching up.

My favorite whipping boys were Chancellor Richard Van Horn and Cougar athletics. Easier targets could not be found. Bill Clements was governor of Texas twice, somehow, and when budget cuts threatened the Technology school at the same time the university had spent $850,000 on an absurd pair of obelisks to mark the entrance to the campus (which you could barely see for all the fast food joints) I went wild. That was the sort of humor I lived for in those days, and going to a state school gave me more grist than my mill could handle.

There really was a student TV station that had its own soap opera. This early story endeared me to the whole crew and the clippings decorated the SVN offices for some time. However, the jabs at the Campus Crusade for Christ types brought down the wrath of God. My first genuine piece of hate mail came from an irate Christian student who suggested maybe next I might like to "brainlessly stereotype" blacks, Jews, or women. I often find it odd that, despite having elected leaders in their pockets, and polls showing that 88% of Americans believe in God, conservative Christians see themselves as an oppressed minority. I suppose if I were to have responded to my "fan," I would have pointed out that, since conservative Christians terrorize blacks under the auspices of the KKK, pump money into the coffers of evangelists who spout "The Lord God does not hear the prayer of a Jew!", and ceaselessly demand sovereignty over the reproductive organs of women whom their Bible tells them must submit to men at all times, they hardly need my help in the "brainless stereotyping" department.

"Bus Ride to Hell," from spring 1987, is perhaps my seminal work in *Shasta Says*, and my favorite story of the period to this date. Based on the actual experiences of a *Cougar* staffer (who told me he wanted to get the "Original Hardass Newsman" panel blown up to poster size), it was the first time I began really paying attention to character. Also, it is noteworthy for the first appearance of the Proto-Gunther. *Vive le difference!*

In January 1987 I transferred to UT-Austin, much to the chagrin of the *Cougar* staff, who offered to put me on salary if I would keep the strip going. I heartily agreed (Jeez, they were gonna *pay* me? Wow!), and *Shasta Says* continued until September 1987, when I was forced to cancel it after the new editor began not getting my jokes and pulling the strip often without warning (the full story of this is told in "Hepcats History 101," *Hepcats* #1—*The Special Edition*). It was just as well. I had started *Hepcats*, and been gone long enough from UH that I probably could no longer have poked at campus peccadilloes with quite the edge I had before. It was time to move on.

I started *Shasta Says* out of boredom and through it I gained a career and a group of wonderful friends on the *Cougar* staff whom I remember fondly to this day. There's a saying here in Texas. What's the prettiest view in the whole state? Houston in your rear view mirror. Having spent 11 years there I'll vouch for that sumbitch in two seconds flat. But I'd like to thank all my old friends at the *Cougar*, and at UH in general, for making my final years in Space City not only bearable, but delightful.

THE DAILY COUGAR STAFF • SPRING 1987

			Michelle Gardner		Stewart Lawrence	Scott Butterworth	Oscar Martinez	
Susan Borreson	Ruthie Piller	Kristin Jacobsen		Mark Evangelista	MW	Jodi Berls, editor (holding Tristan)		Emily Smith

Photographer unknown

Daily Cougar

'COUGAR' REPORTER GOES TO ICELAND TO COVER SUMMIT

INTREPID JOURNALIST

ALIENS DISINTEGRATE OBELISKS WITH HEAT RAY

WELL, ERIN, THAT WAS QUITE A COUP SENDING A SENIOR WRITER TO ICELAND.

I THOUGHT SO. EMILY IS SURE TO WIN US AN AWARD OR TWO.

EMILY!? I DIDN'T KNOW YOU SENT EMILY!!

YEAH, SHE OUGHT TO BE AT THE PRESS CONFERENCE RIGHT NOW, IN FACT.

COULD YOU STAND UP, PLEASE MISS?

I AM STANDING UP!!

MORNING. A NEW DAY DAWNS ON GOOD OL' UNIVERSITY PARK. STUDENTS PREPARE FOR NEW DAY OF HIGHER EDUCATION...

EZIEKEL W. CULLEN BUILDING

HEY!

THIS UNIVERSITY CONDEMNED BY B. CLEMENTS'

COMMANDO COST-CUTTERS

OUR MOTTO: "STATE SCHOOLS BEND OVER!"

YES... HOT ON THE HEELS OF THE ELECTION RESULTS, THE COMMANDOS SWEPT DOWN ON UNIVERSITY PARK OVER THE WEEKEND.

IN THE REMAINS OF THE STUDENT LIFE BUILDING, THE FAMILIAR CRY WAS BEGUN...

HANG ON, BOSS. HELP IS COMING.

WHERE? WHERE ON THIS CAMPUS IS THERE ANY MORE MONEY!? *COUGH!*

BILL, WE ALL TOOK A POOL AND BOUGHT YOU THIS ROLEX!

AWW... Y'ALL SHOULDN'T HAVE!

FOR HE'S A JOLLY GOOD FELLOW!

NOW ENTERING ATHLETIC DEPT. PROSTRATE YOURSELF

SO LONG, COACH YEOMAN!

HOLY COW! WHAT HAPPENED TO THE LIBRARY?

HUH! YOU SHOULDA BEEN HERE OVER THE WEEKEND.

I WAS SCRUBBIN' TOILETS IN THE BLUE WING WHEN I HEARD ALLA THIS NOISE. WENT UPSTAIRS AND SAW ALLA THESE GUYS WEARIN' FATIGUES WITH "GUV'NER BILL" ON THEIR BACKS IN BIG RED LETTERS TAKIN' EV'RYTHING NOT NAILED DOWN.

WHAT!?! WHY!?

'S THE ECONOMY. IT SEEMS OUR NEW GUV'NER IS GONNA HOLD A BIG GARAGE SALE AT THE MANSION ON INAUGURATION DAY AN' SINK THE MONEY INTO THE OIL BIZNESS.

BUT... BUT WHAT ABOUT MY EDUCATION!? WHAT ABOUT MY FUTURE!?

YOU THINK YOU'RE MAD! KUHF JUST DUMPED JAZZ.

YES, ALTHOUGH THANKSGIVING HAS NOT YET DAWNED, THE SPIRIT OF CHRISTMAS HAS ALREADY BEGUN TO MANIFEST ITSELF AT UNIVERSITY PARK.

ΔΨ PRESENT XMAS BEER

THE ADMINISTRATION, IN THE CRYSTAL PALACE OF E. CULLEN, BRAINSTORMS NEW IDEAS TO CRANK UP A FESTIVE MOOD.

C'MON, DICK. IT'S **PR!**

WILL YOU GET OUT OF MY DAMN OFFICE!?

11-18

MEANWHILE, STUDENTS IN UP'S FINE RESIDENCE HALLS RECEIVE THEIR FIRST HOLIDAY GREETING CARDS FROM THAT SELFSAME, AUGUST BODY!

You're evicted!

YOU CAN'T EVICT ME! I'M FROM OVERSEAS! I HAVE NOWHERE ELSE TO STAY WHILE I'M ON HOLIDAY!

BUT YOU DO, SIR! WE CAN RELOCATE YOU TO THESE APARTMENTS FOR ONLY $300!

CAMPUS HOUSING

AND WHERE AM I SUPPOSED TO GET 300 SODDING DOLLARS IN 30 DAYS!?

LOOK, YOU **SHOULD** HAVE SEEN THIS COMING! IT'S IN YOUR LEASE!

CAMPUS HOUSING!?

IT IS?

YEAH! RIGHT THERE! SMALL PRINT!

CAMPUS HOUSING

"WE RESERVE THE RIGHT TO KICK YOU OUT ON YOUR BUTT AT THE LAST MINUTE."

AS YOU CAN SEE, IT'S VERY CLEAR.

CAMPUS HOUSIN

MR. VAN HORN, EXACTLY HOW DO YOU PLAN TO BATTLE THIS "SECOND-TIER" BUSINESS?

WELL, WITH EVERYTHING I'VE GOT, OF COURSE!

11-20

THIS "TIER" BUSINESS IS AN UTTER **OUTRAGE!** TO RELEGATE OUR FINE UNIVERSITY TO SECOND-CLASS STATUS WILL BE NOTHING BUT INTELLECTUAL EUTHANASIA FOR OUR STUDENTS!

WRITE WRITE

WE'VE GOT A **FINE** FACULTY! SURE, WE HAVE FINANCIAL TROUBLE BUT WHO **DOESN'T** RIGHT NOW? OUR STUDENT SERVICES ARE SO EXEMPLARY THEY PUT U.T. & A&M TO **SHAME!**

METRO

U.H. INT'L STUDENT HOMELESS FREEZING GOT A

WHAT ON EARTH?

LEAVE IT TO THE **STUDENT PROGRAM BOARD** TO COME UP WITH A WAY TO SOLVE THE DORM CRISIS!

11-21

TOO LOUD? TOO LOUD. **TOO LOUD!** TOO LOUD? TOO LOUD.

Marshall

DORM AID

YO, CATS! WELCOME TO DORM-AID, THE BENEFIT CONCERT FOR ALL THE DORMIES PITCHED INTO THE COLD BY THE FASCIST VAN HORN REGIME!!

NOW WE'RE GONNA DO A SONG THAT WE THINK CAPTURES THE SEETHING FURY OF THE DORMITORY SUBCULTURE! READY! 1-2-3---

SHOUT SHOUT, LET IT ALL OUT...

IT'S TIMES LIKE THESE I BEGIN TO GET THE IDEA THAT THE NOBILITY OF OUR GOALS IS OVERSHADOWED BY THE EXTREME SILLINESS OF OUR METHODS!

WELL, JON OL' BUDDY, ONLY A FEW MORE WEEKS UNTIL CHRISTMAS! LOOKIN' FORWARD TO IT, HUH?

AGNES ARNOLD HALL

UH-U

YEAH, GOING BACK HOME TO SEE PARENTS AND BROTHERS AND SISTERS AND RELATIVES AND EAT A **BIG** HOLIDAY DINNER! IT ALMOST MAKES THE WHOLE SEMESTER WORTHWHILE.

JON...JON, YOU OKAY...?

ISN'T IT **PRECIOUS?** AND IT WAS ON SALE!

UH, THANKS, MOM. WHENEVER I USE THIS I'LL... THINK OF YOU.

I WANNA SEE! I WANNA SEE!

GHOSTS OF CHRISTMASES PAST WHISK THROUGH JON'S TROUBLED MIND.

C'MON, JUDY, LET ME HELP!

OH, DON'T BE SILLY.

@$!! FLASH!

LOOK, DAD, IT'S THIS SWITCH.

CHRISSY, DON'T BEAT UP YOUR BROTHER.

HE STARTED IT!

WAAHH!

GOD. HERSHEY'S KISSES. I MUST'VE EATEN THREE THOUSAND OF THESE THINGS.

C'MON, BIG BROTHER! LET'S PLAY "LAZER TAG"!!

COUGARS

OKAY, JON... QUIT GOOFIN' AROUND! TIME TO GET INTO THE HOLIDAY SPIRIT. AND WHAT BETTER WAY TO DO THAT THAN BY PLAYING "LAZER TAG" WITH YOUR SNOTTY KID BROTHER?

STEALTHILY THE "LAZER TAG" WARRIOR CREEPS THROUGH THE HOSTILE JUNGLE WILDERNESS OF THE PLANET TRANTORIUS.

THEN, SPOTTING HIS ARCH-NEMESIS, HE LEAPS FROM THE TANGLED VINES WITH A FIERCE BATTLE CRY...

YAAAA!

WHEREUPON A MISCALCULATION IN TRAJECTORY LANDS HIM SMACK IN THE MIDDLE OF THE BACKYARD POOL.

SOME "MASTER OF THE UNIVERSE" **YOU** ARE.

SO IN A COUPLE OF DAYS I'LL BE GOING BACK HOME TO SEE MY FOLKS.

OH, JON, DOESN'T THE CHRISTMAS SEASON MAKE YOU WANT TO PUT IT ALL ASIDE AND BE A KID AGAIN?

NAH.

ME NEITHER.

WELL, ONCE AGAIN THE SUN RISES ON A NEW SEMESTER AT UNIVERSITY PARK.

BUT EVEN AS THE STUDENT BODY FROLICKED OVER THE YULETIDE, THE GREAT BRAINS OF THE CAMPUS DID NOT REST.

FSSS! BUBBLE! BLURP!

SCRIBBLE SCRIBBLE

YES, EVEN AS OLD ST. NICK CRUISED THE GLOBE, CLOGGING CHIMNEYS WORLD-WIDE WITH GENUINE ELF-MADE TOYS, HISTORY WAS IN THE MAKING.

IT'S A BREAK-THROUGH IN ELECTRICAL ENGINEERING!

WHOA, DUDE!

EVENTS SO ASTONISHING, IN FACT, THAT EVEN THE TEXAS LEGISLATURE TOOK NOTICE.

Your work is so remarkable that Governor Clements _almost_ regrets cutting off all of your funding.

TIKKA TIKKA TIKKA

SO WHAT WE'VE DEVELOPED IS A MEANS BY WHICH ELECTRICITY CAN TRAVEL WITH NO RESISTANCE.

THAT'S NEAT, PHIL.

NEAT!? FOR CHRISSAKES, IT'S THE MOST IMPORTANT SCIENTIFIC DEVELOPMENT SINCE THE ⚡💢!!@# POLIO VACCINE! NOW HOW CAN YOU CUT OUR FUNDING!?

IT'S NOT ME, PHIL.

MONEY'S TIGHT, PHIL. YOU KNOW WE HAVE TO PRIORITIZE.

DON'T TELL ME, DICK. I DON'T WANT TO KNOW.

WHOA, DUDE! NEW SHOULDER PADS!

THAT'S NOTHIN' MAN! COME CHECK OUT MY NEW MERCEDES.

PROPERTY OF COUGAR

WHAT'S GOING ON?

DOC'S LOCKED HIMSELF IN THE LAB!

HE CAME IN TODAY MUTTER-ING SOMETHING ABOUT "PETTY BUREAUCRATS," AND THEN...

BAM BAM

KA-**BLAM**

AAAAIIEE!!

VENGEANCE ...IS MINE.

GOD, I THINK HE HIT HIS HEAD!

THEY THINK THEY CAN STEAL OUR MONEY!? HA!

I HAVE SOME MIDOL!

SHUT UP AND CALL RED ADAIR!

Page 124

125

RENEÉ, DID YOU HEAR ABOUT BRUCE?

YOU MEAN "MR. PIN-UP 1988?" YES! I ALMOST **DIED!**

AREN'T YOU AFRAID THIS IS GONNA PUMP HIS EGO TO DOUBLE-SIZE? IT'S AS BIG AS THE MOON ALREADY!

DON'T WORRY, ANGIE. THE WHOLE SORORITY IS TAKING MATTERS IN HAND.

OH, NO! YOU MEAN...?

STEP ONE INVOLVES THE STRATEGIC PLACEMENT OF POSTERS ON CAMPUS...

GOD, RENEÉ! YOU WANT TO GIVE HIM A HEART ATTACK!?

JUST A LITTLE ONE.

BRUCE MEGASTUD, 499-1031 BY APPOINTMENT ONLY! (HEALTH RECORDS UPON REQUEST)

ANY RESEMBLANCE TO ACTUAL PHONE NUMBERS IS JUST YOUR BAD LUCK.

OKAY, GIRLS! WHEN HE GETS OUT OF THE STUDIO, YOU KNOW WHAT TO DO!

RENEÉ, THIS IS SO **FUNNY!**

HERE HE COMES!

SHRIEEEEEEEEK!!

GAAH!

RENEÉ, I SAID THIS MIGHT HAPPEN.

BRUCE, HONEY, COME ON, WE WERE JOKING.

WELL, I CERTAINLY HOPE ONE OF YOU LADIES KNOWS C.P.R.

COME ON, BRUCE! BE REASONABLE!

NO! FORGET IT! THE HELL WITH THIS CALENDAR CRAP — I'M **THROUGH!**

BUT, BRUCE, WE'RE ON THE WIRE! WE DON'T HAVE TIME TO HIRE ANOTHER MODEL!

DUDE, IF YOU'D BEEN THROUGH WHAT I'VE BEEN THROUGH THIS WEEK...

WE'LL PAY YOU AN EXTRA 25 BUCKS FOR TODAY.

OH! UH... WELL...

WAIT A MINUTE... 25 BUCKS WON'T EVEN BUY A KEG!

HEY!

FLASH!

KLIK!

OKAY, THAT'S A WRAP! PACK IT IN, GUYS!

DAMN IT, I WASN'T READY!

CLICK! KLIK!

DON'T BE SILLY, BRUCE. YOU DID GREAT! CHECK'S IN THE MAIL! ...OKAY, GUYS, WHO'S BUYIN' THE PIZZA?

BUT... HEY... BUT...

Kodak

Houston's **HAIREST**

PRESENTED BY CAMPUS AWARENESS

MEN OF U.H. **1988**

WELL, B
YOUR PL
REALL
OUT

EXCUSE ME... I WANT TO MAKE AN "EQUAL-TIME" COMMENT.

I REPRESENT THE **N.O.W.-AT-U.H. ANTI-PORNOGRAPHY TASK FORCE.** THIS "HOUSTON'S HOTTEST" CALENDAR NONSENSE IS JUST MORE DEGRADING, MISOGYNISTIC **SLEAZE** THAT HAS NO BUSINESS AT AN INSTITUTION OF HIGHER EDUCATION!

WOMEN OF U.H.

CONSCIENTIOUS STUDENTS HAVE A RESPONSIBILITY TO BOYCOTT THE WHOLE MESS ...EVEN THIS...THIS **NEW** CALENDAR... WITH **MEN** IN IT...ER...

FLIP FLIP

U OF H WOMEN

ANYWAY, AS I WAS SAYING... **HEY!**

GOT OUT MIND!

SORRY... BACK TO THE STRIP.

WHAT'S THAT?

OH, IT'S THIS STUPID "HOUSTON'S HOTTEST" PIN-UP CALENDER.

NOW

YOU CAN'T GO **ANYWHERE** THESE DAYS WITHOUT RUNNING INTO SMUT, CAN YOU?

YOU SAID IT! I PLAN TO USE THIS IN MY TALK ON "PORN ON CAMPUS" THIS AFTERNOON.

WELL, GOOD LUCK. I'VE GOTTA RUN. ...BY THE WAY, I HAVE THAT BOOK YOU WANTED TO BORROW!

OH, **GOOD!** SHE'S MY FAVORITE AUTHOR! NOW I CAN TAKE MY MIND OFF THIS **FILTH** FOR A WHILE!

"Oh, Blake!" she cried, but there was fire and passion in her voice as the virile ad executive crushed her in his tanned, muscular arms. A gasp of wanton desire escaped her as he hungrily thrust his aching manhood deeper and deeper beyond th hold of her virtue. Sh   "Oh, Blake, stop," b   art was not in her   ad she threw her le   midriff and return   motions with   Never ha   arefree ab   since th

"WOW!" -PHIL DENAME

JACKIE COLLINS IN JUMBO

HOTTEST!

3/3

ALL RIGHT, KID, THIS IS YOUR FIRST BIG STORY, SO DON'T SCREW UP! IT'S ALL ABOUT PORNOGRAPHY ON CAMPUS.

TIMBUK

YESSIR, MR. EVANGELIST, SIR!

EVANGELIST**A**. NOW LISTEN! I NEED INTERVIEWS! CASE HISTORIES! CHRIST, BUY SOME DIRTY BOOKS IF YA HAVE TO! BUT MAKE IT GOOD!

WELL... UH...

WHAT'S THE PROBLEM NOW?

TIMBUK3

I'M ONLY 19, SIR.

THAT'S JUST FOR DRINKING, KID. SWEATING'S OKAY.

pat pat

HI! I'M A WRITER FOR THE COUGAR. COULD I ASK YOU SOME QUESTIONS ABOUT STUDENT REACTION TO ADULT MAGAZINES HERE?

UH

3-6

YEAH. WELL, THEY'RE NO BIG DEAL, REALLY.

"The campus is up in arms about this."

SCRIBBLE

BASICALLY, WE DO MUCH BETTER BUSINESS IN THE GENERAL MAGAZINES.

"Demand is so high, we have a waiting list."

WRITE WRITE

UH

HALF THE TIME I DON'T EVEN KNOW THEY'RE HERE.

"My close daily proximity to them has turned me into an avowed baby-rapist!"

SCRIBBLE

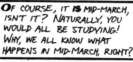

"NATURALLY, A CRUCIAL ASPECT OF DORM LIFE IS GETTING TO KNOW YOUR ROOMIE..."

SO, DAVE. YOU'RE AN AD MAJOR?

YEAH! I'M WORKING ON THIS CAMPAIGN TO PROMOTE PUBLIC AWARENESS IN SAFE SEX!

Use Spunko® Condoms

or die a horrible, lingering death.

PRETTY AGGRESSIVE, HUH?

"FAMILY CIRCLE" MIGHT HAVE PROBLEMS WITH IT.

"DESPITE **U.T.**'s CANDIDACY FOR 'FIRST-TIER STATUS,' VARIOUS DEPARTMENTS OF THE CAMPUS CLAIM TO BE **LOSING MONEY**... JUST LIKE **US!** (HMM!) IT'S IN THE PAPERS..."

DAILY TEXAN

We're losing money!

Oral Roberts explodes Check bounces

"...YOU CAN ASK THE **SCIENCE DEPARTMENTS**..."

WHY, JUST LAST WEEK, I PETITIONED FOR MORE FUNDING FOR RADIO SPECTROMETRY RESEARCH AND WAS TOLD I'D HAVE TO SEEK A **PRIVATE GRANT!**

"...YOU CAN ASK THE **ARTS & HUMANITIES**..."

BRILLIANT, ISN'T HE? DAMN SHAME HE'LL HAVE TO PAINT OVER IT FOR THE NEXT ONE.

Sniff!

"...WHY, EVEN **THEIR** ATHLETIC DEPARTMENT CLAIMS TO BE **FINANCIALLY EMBATTLED!**"

NCAA VIOLATIONS? CHRIST, IF WE COULD AFFORD 'EM, MAYBE WE WOULD!

MARTIN WAGNER'S SHASTA SAYS

HORRIFYING TRUE TALES: the Final Chapter

©1987 MW

THUS, ROVING REPORTER/CARTOONIST "PINK-NOSE" COMPLETES HIS STUDY OF U.T., STILL UNSURE IF A "TIER" SYSTEM MAKES SENSE, MUCH LESS WHO SHOULD BE AT THE TOP OF IT.

ONE THING, HOWEVER, HE **IS** SURE OF...

WELCOME HOME!

Sigh

JEEZ. I JUST CAN'T CONCENTRATE ON THIS STUFF!

MIGHT AS WELL CRAM FOR SUMMER INSTEAD. IT'LL BE HERE BEFORE YA KNOW IT. YEP, JUST BASKING IN THE SUN...

BASKING...BASKING...

YAIEE!

RELAX! I HAVEN'T EVEN OPENED THE BOTTLE YET!

SO WHAT'S THIS I HEAR ABOUT YOUR SISTER GETTING PARBOILED?

OH, MOM! SHE'S OKAY.

YOU KNOW WHAT EXPOSURE LIKE THAT CAN **DO** TO YOU!?

SO HOW'S DAD?

FINE....LOOK, JUST MAKE SURE SHE USES A LOT OF MOISTURIZER!

SHE'S FINE, MOM. SHE'S IN THE BEDROOM WITH THOSE MAGAZINES YOU KEEP SENDING.

Women face new cancer risks

"If the skin doesn't go, the boobs will," warn experts.

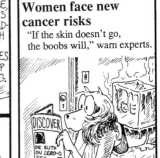

4-16

WELL, HERE SHE IS, FOLKS! "JOAN OF ARC," HOME FROM CLASS! HOW'D YOU HOLD OUT?

OH, OKAY. I'M FINALLY STARTING TO PEEL.

DON'T WORRY. A BURN LIKE THAT CAN'T BE ANY WORSE THAN SLEEPING WITH YOUR MAKEUP ON.

HUH?

IT AGES YOUR SKIN SEVEN YEARS. DIDN'T YOU KNOW THAT?

SCRUB SCRUB SCRUB

4-17

SHASTA SAYS presents *MARK EVANGELISTA*

THE ORIGINAL HARDASS NEWSMAN in *BUS RIDE TO HELL*

*FREELY BASED UPON THE 1987 SPRING BREAK MEMOIRS OF **M.E.**, AS IMMORTALIZED ON THE FRONT PAGE OF THE "DAILY COUGAR," MARCH 27, 1987.*

AH, AMERICA! OH BEAUTIFUL FOR SPACIOUS SKIES!

YOU KNOW, IT OCCURED TO ME, DURING A BLINDING RUSH OF SOBRIETY, THAT WHAT I **REALLY** WANTED TO DO THIS SPRING BREAK WAS SIT BACK AND **SEE** AMERICA IN **ALL ITS GLORY**... AND TOWARD THAT END, I PICKED THE MOST **PASSIVE** TOUR OPTION I COULD FIND!

4-21

"I TOOK THE **BUS!**"

FORM ONE LINE HERE

ASTRI

CONTINUED...

FROM THE SPRING BREAK MEMOIRS OF MARK EVANGELISTA, FOUND IN A HIGHWAY REST-STOP TOILET 35 MI. OUTSIDE CHEYENNE, WYOMING: "WHEN I DECIDED TO TAKE THE **GREYHOUND** TO VISIT MY GRANDPARENTS IN **SAN FRANCISCO**, I KNEW I WAS IN FOR A CULTURAL EXPERIENCE."

"IT OCCURED TO ME HOW MUCH THERE IS WE TAKE FOR GRANTED ABOUT OUR COUNTRY"

4-22

"HOW THERE'S SO MANY DIFFERENT WALKS OF LIFE THAT WE NEVER EVEN SEE IN OUR BUSTLING URBAN LIVES."

POOT!

I COULD PROBABLY WRITE A **BEST-SELLER** ABOUT MY JOURNEY INTO THE HEARTLAND!

BEER-BELLIED JOHN STIENBECK IMITATORS IN THE BACK.

UH

HIYA, BUDDY! I'M JETHRO BLODGETT FROM JACKSONVILLE, TEXAS! PUT 'ER THERE!

SO WHEREYA GOIN', BUD? ME, AH'M UP TA RENO TA SEE TH' OLD MAN! MY PAPPY DONE HAD HIM A TRIPLE CORONARY BYPASS! HYUK HYUK!

SLAP

AH TOL' HIM, "PAPPY, YOU QUIT SMOKIN' THEM 17 PACKS O' CAMELS A DAY, YOU WON'T NEED NO SURGERY!" AIN'T THAT RIGHT? WHADDAYA SAY, PAL!?

I SAY IF YOU DON'T SHUT UP IN TWO SECONDS I'M GONNA DO SOME SURGERY **ON YOU!**

WELL, POKE ME RUNNIN'! MY PAPPY SAID THE SAME THANG!

BUS RIDE TO **HELL:** THE SAGA CONTINUES SOMEWHERE NEAR THE ROCKIES.

WHAT THE ⚡💀📢!!✴

GREYHOUND

BAM!

UH, SORRY, FOLKS. JUST RAN OVER A COUPLE OF MATING WOODCHUCKS. LOST A REAR TIRE. THIS MIGHT TAKE A FEW MINUTES.

YEAH? WELL, IF THEY DIDN'T LET DAGO GIMP-BRAINS INTO THE WORK FORCE, MAYBE WE'D GET WHERE WE WERE GOING!

THAT'S IT. NO MORE "DEAD KENNEDYS" TAPES ON LONG ROAD TRIPS.

PICTURES FROM THE ROAD:

LIMIT 55

The rolling countryside, outside my window.

4-29

Nasty little kid in row ahead of me. Still amazed I let him live.

Awesome babe two rows back I was too nervous to meet. Am working on some romantic anecdotes to impress Erin with.

REST STOP

MEN

Me, self-portrait. Grand Canyon not in background.

SO, MARK, WHAT DO YOU DO?

I REVIEW MUSIC FOR A COLLEGE PAPER.

GREYHOUND

4-24

A MUSIC CRITIC? SO, YOU PROBABLY THINK SPRINGSTEEN IS GOD, HUH?

WELL, I'M RESERVING THAT FOR ROBERT CRAY, LATELY.

TELL ME, WHAT DO YOU THINK OF WAYNE NEWTON?

OH, FOR GOD'S **SAKE!** DON'T TELL ME YOU ACTUALLY LISTEN TO THAT SIMPED-OUT WUSSIE!?

NO...NO... I'M ONE OF HIS MAFIA GODCHILDREN.

YOU KNOW, FOR A WUSSIE, NEWTON'S GOT **ONE CLASS ACT!**

THE SHASTA SAYS ADJUSTMENT GUIDE FOR INCOMING FRESHMEN

Part 3: BEING A COLLEGE KID

NATURALLY, THERE WILL BE SIGNIFICANT LIFESTYLE CHANGES TO BE MADE DURING YOUR TRANSITION FROM HIGH SCHOOL TO COLLEGE. BUT WITH A LITTLE DETERMINATION, ALL CAN GO SMOOTHLY. SO PRICK UP YOUR EARS, DUST OFF YOUR FAKE I.D., AND LET "SHASTA SAYS" INTRODUCE YOU TO YOUR BRAVE NEW WORLD.

9-4 ©1987 Martin Wagner

HOMESICKNESS: ACTUALLY, AT U.H., THERE'S A 70% CHANCE YOU'RE STILL LIVING AT HOME, SO FOR YOU, "HOMESICKNESS" MEANS "SICK OF HOME." IT COULD LEAD YOU TO TRANSFER AFTER YOUR SOPHOMORE YEAR.

YO, I'M HOME!

GREAT! HELP ME BRING IN THE GROCERIES!

MONEY PROBLEMS: EVERYBODY'S GOT 'EM, SO TOUGH BUNS.

ACCOUNT OVERDRAWN. PREPARE TO DIE.

STUDY: MAY AS WELL. JEEZ. THE BOOKS COST ENOUGH.

BOTANY / CALCULUS / ECONOMICS / DRIVEL

GOING GREEK: FOR MANY FRESHMEN, THIS IS THE MOST IMPORTANT ASPECT OF COLLEGE. IF YOU GO FOR THAT TYPE OF CLIQUISHNESS, JUST MAKE SURE YOU HAVE A HIGH TOLERANCE FOR:
• PHYSICAL ABUSE. (LOTS OF IT.)
• INCESSANT HANGOVERS.
• DATING ONLY WHOM YOU'RE TOLD.
• BURNOUT BY AGE 20.

AΩ

CONTINUED NEXT WEDNESDAY...

THE SHASTA SAYS ADJUSTMENT GUIDE FOR INCOMING FRESHMEN

Part 4: FOOD AND HOUSING

OKAY, AS WE SAID BEFORE, U.H. IS A COMMUTER SCHOOL, HONESTLY, SO MOST OF YOU ARE IN YOUR OWN HOMES...

BUT... FOR THOSE OF YOU WHO HAVE DECIDED TO GIVE ON-CAMPUS LIVING A TRY, HERE'S A QUICK CHECKLIST TO HELP YOU OUT. ➡

©1987 Martin Wagner 9-9

1 MOODY TOWERS ARE:
A: SWELL.
B: I'D RATHER LIVE IN PGH's ELEVATORS.

2 THE MEAL PLAN IS:
A: JUST LIKE MOM'S HOME COOKING.
B: OKAY, THOUGH I HAVE TO CUT MY STEAK WITH A PROPANE TORCH.
C: BAD ENOUGH TO MAKE ME SALIVATE OVER THE IDEA OF EATING ANOTHER GREASY, PAPER CHEESEBURGER AT THE SATELLITE.

3 MY ROOM IS:
A: LUXURY ITSELF.
B: ABOUT THE SIZE OF THE LETTERING IN THIS CARTOON.

4 MY ROOMMATE HAS JUST STUMBLED IN AT 5:39 A.M. AND PUKED A MASSIVE DELUGE ONTO THE FLOOR. I:
A: AM THANKFULLY TOO BLITZED MYSELF TO CARE.
B: KILL HIM/HER IN A FIT OF MORAL OUTRAGE.
C: LAUGH JOVIALLY AND WIPE UP THE MESS WITH A "SHASTA SAYS" T-SHIRT.

5 ON THE WHOLE I:
A: LOVE IT!
B: WANT MY OWN APARTMENT
C: WISH TO GOD I WAS 21.

Now Score Yourself!

CHILL OUT— THIS WON'T COUNT TOWARD YOUR GPA.

QUESTION 1: A-1, B-3
QUESTION 2: A-1, B-4, C-2
QUESTION 3: A-1, B-7
QUESTION 4: A-7, B-5, C-1
QUESTION 5: A-1, B-4, C-3

Results:
• 20-25: CONGRATULATIONS ON YOUR SPLENDID ADJUSTMENT!
• 6-19: YOU'RE DOIN' OKAY, BUT EXPECT TO GO THROUGH MID-LIFE CRISIS IN A BIG WAY.
• 1-5: YOU WUSSIE!

ONE LAST WORD

THUNKA THUNKA

IF YOUR ROOMIE HAS AN "OVERNIGHT GUEST"...RETALIATE HOWEVER YOU WISH, BUT DON'T TURN 'EM IN!

SOMEDAY, YOU MAY GET LUCKY, TOO!

THE SHASTA SAYS ADJUSTMENT GUIDE FOR INCOMING FRESHMEN

Part 5: THE CAMPUS POLICE ARE YOUR FRIENDS

HERE ARE SOME PEOPLE WE THINK YOU SHOULD GET TO KNOW VERY WELL. AFTER ALL, HAVE YOU EVER REALLY WONDERED WHY THERE'S SUCH A PARKING PROBLEM ON CAMPUS? IT'S SIMPLE! IF WE HAD MORE SPACES THE CAMPUS POLICE WOULD LOSE $17 ZILLION A YEAR FROM TICKETS!

★↓@#!! KIDS! THINK THEY CAN PARK ANY-WHERE.

Landau

NOT TO MAKE YOU NERVOUS OR ANYTHING, BUT U.H. IS NOT EXACTLY THE SAFEST PART OF TOWN, AND CRIMES DO OCCUR! BUT NEVER FEAR...

ALWAYS REMEMBER THE POLICEMAN IS YOUR FRIEND, EVEN THOUGH HE IS THE MOST OVER-WORKED, UNDERPAID, AND SLIGHTED PUBLIC SERVANT IN THE COUNTRY.

AND WITH THAT IN MIND, HERE'S **WHAT TO DO IF YOU ARE VICTIMIZED ON CAMPUS:**

DURING THE DAY:
• STAGGER TO THE NEAREST STUDENT PARKING LOT TO FIND A COP. (SEE ILLUSTRATION)
• REPORT THE CRIME.
AT NIGHT:
• OH, WELL...

BE WITH YA IN A MINUTE...

TOMORROW: CHAPTER THE LAST.

©1987 MW 9-10

THE SHASTA SAYS ADJUSTMENT GUIDE FOR INCOMING FRESHMEN

Part 6: CLASS

!YEAH, YEAH...

WE WANNA AVOID THIS TOPIC JUST AS MUCH AS YOU, BUT, YOU KNOW, YOU REALLY SHOULD REMEMBER WHY YOU'RE HERE...

9-11 ©1987 Martin Wagner

INTIMIDATING, ISN'T IT?!?

THERE YOU SIT IN THE LECTURE HALL, AND MY GOD, THERE MUST BE 200 OTHER PEOPLE IN THERE — BUT IT DOESN'T MAKE ANY DIFFERENCE! YOU'RE STILL ON YOUR OWN!!

GULP!

YES, IT'S TRUE! THAT WHOLE AUTHORITARIAN DISCIPLINE TRIP THEY LAID ON YOU THROUGHOUT GRADES K-12 GOES UP IN A PUFF OF SMOKE IN COLLEGE! NOT ONLY CAN YOU DO STUFF LIKE COME TO CLASS IN SHORTS

...IF YOU SCREW UP...

NO ONE SENDS A PROGRESS REPORT...

NO ONE CALLS YOUR FOLKS...

IT'S GREAT! [THEY JUST KILL YOU ON THE FINAL!]

NOW, SINCE MOST FRESHMAN CLASSES ARE BIG, YOU'LL PROBABLY HAVE TEACHERS' ASSISTANTS!

HI! MY NAME IS SUNBEAM, AND I'M A POET!

BUT JUST 'COS A T.A. IS CLOSE TO YOUR AGE DOESN'T MEAN YOU'LL RELATE TO THEM.

2 IMPORTANT QUESTIONS ANSWERED!

DO I NEED A TUTOR?

YEP.

FOR WHAT CLASS?

ALL OF 'EM.

134

HEPCATS

Number One

The first issue of *Hepcats* was drawn through the winter of 1988-89. It was a time of transition, during which, among other things, I met my soon-to-be-ex-wife. The book was printed in Austin by John Nordland II, who self-published his book *Heroes* under the Blackbird Comics imprint. John had tremendous problems completing the print run, due to the fact that the sheet-fed press he had bought (talk about self-publishing!) was an utter lemon and he simply could not get reliable service on it. What's worse, someone at the 1989 San Diego Comic Con started spreading a rumor that I had been bad-mouthing John at the con, which was patently untrue, and he and I had a personal falling out that lasted more than a year. Over third-party interference.

So I'd like to take this opportunity to publicly thank John for all the work and personal sacrifice he endured to help get my book out to the light of day. Bad things happen to good people, and unfortunately *Hepcats* #1 had to happen all over John Nordland.

The issue was reviewed very favorably in *Amazing Heroes* #169 by Mark Scott Marcus. Sales were right around six thousand, a level I have yet to reattain, after 11 issues, by early 1993. But it'll get there.

Whenever there is nudity, however brief, in a comic, *somebody* out there has a very large cow. Whatever the case, Joey's sex-fantasy sequence that makes up the first half of this issue remains a favorite of many fans. And I think it's clear that he's the butt of the joke. Some people are just so doggone uptight.

Original title page art to *Hepcats* #1.

PART I

JOEY GUNTHER

BONG
BONG
BONG
BON
B

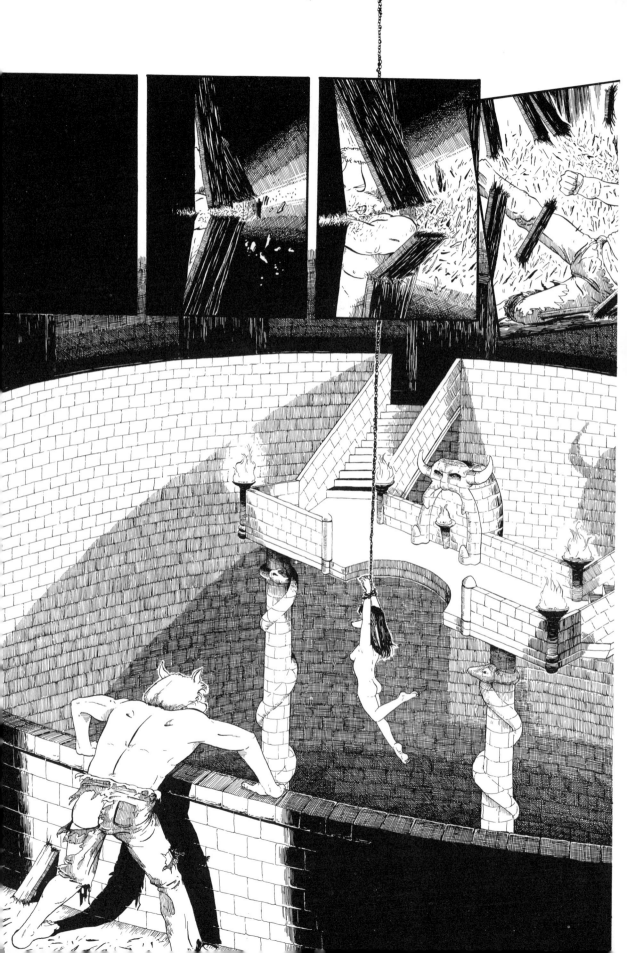

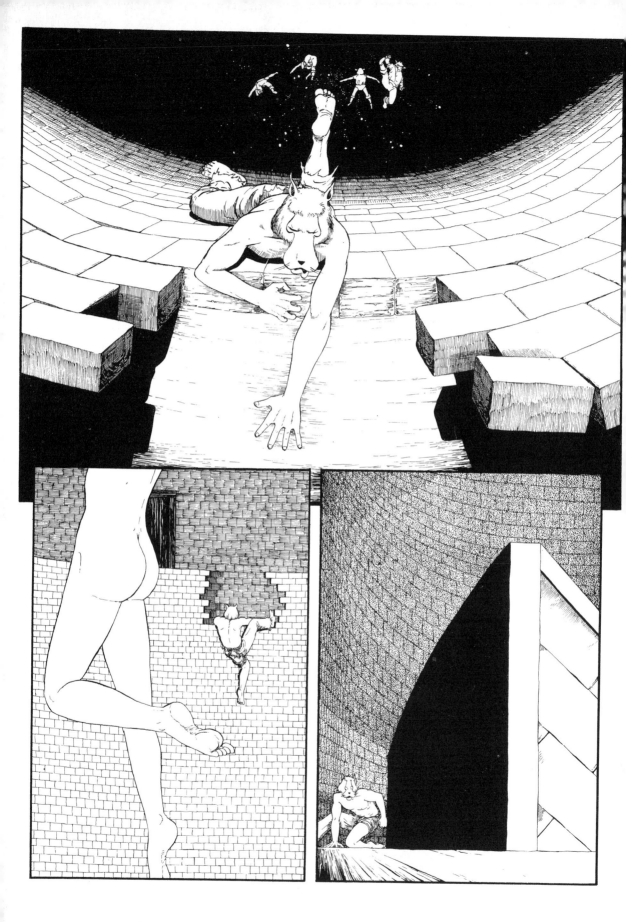

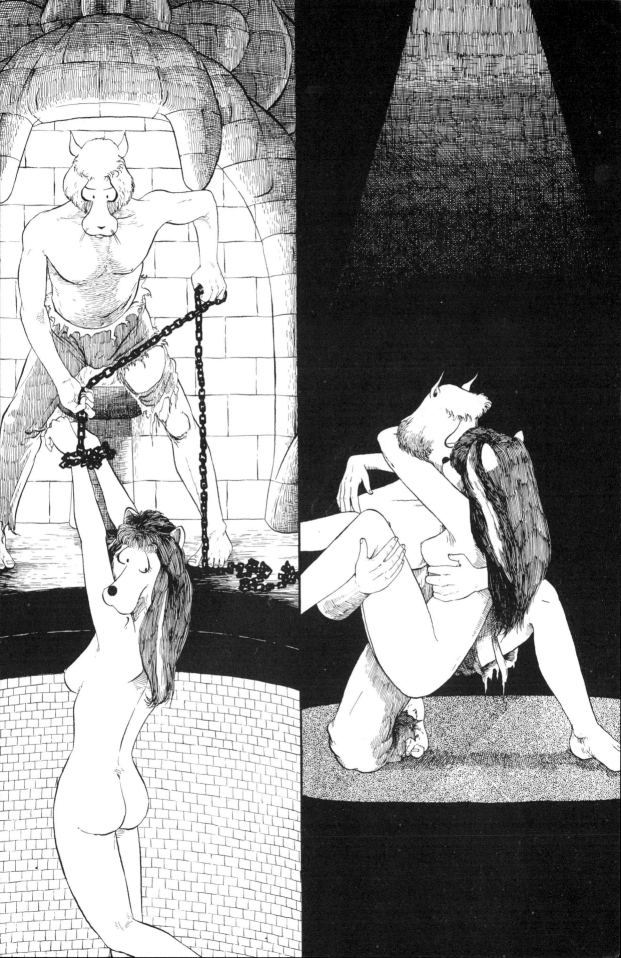

POP!

JOEY!

GUNTHER! SO HOW DID THE ACCOUNTING TEST FROM HELL GO?

BEAUTIFUL! JUST BEAUTIFUL! I MANAGED TO GET THE WHOLE THING DOWN ON ONE SIDE OF A 3x5 CARD!

GUESS I BLEW THE CURVE FOR EVERYBODY ELSE.

AHH, WELL.

BY THE WAY, DID YOU REMEMBER TO PAY THE RENT?

GREAT! SO I GUESS WE'RE DUMPSTER-DIVING FOR DINNER TONIGHT?

HEY SORRY, OKAY? I THOUGHT YOU HAD THE CHECK!

OH, FUCK IT. LET'S GO SHOOT SOME POOL. I'M HAVING A GOOD DAY!

WELL, I'M NOT! AND I DON'T MUCH FEEL LIKE LETTING IT GET ANY WORSE!

AW, CHEER UP. BESIDES, I'M PAYING!

ALL RIGHT, ALL RIGHT....

152

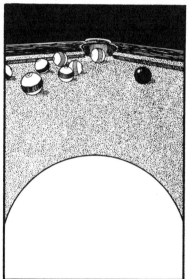

HEPCatS

MARTIN WAGNER was born in Henderson, Nevada on April 27, 1966. Throughout his childhood he lived with his family in the United Kingdom, Dubai, and Singapore. He currently lives in Austin, Texas, where he is hard at work on the next issue of *Hepcats*.